W. D. Billings

DUKE UNIVERSITY

# PLANTS
# AND
# THE ECOSYSTEM

**WADSWORTH PUBLISHING COMPANY, INC.**
**Belmont, California**

FUNDAMENTALS
OF
BOTANY
SERIES

edited by
WILLIAM A. JENSEN,
University of California
LEROY G. KAVALJIAN,
Sacramento State College

TO SHIRLEY

Sixth printing: June 1969

L. C. Cat. Card No.: 64-21770

PHOTOLITHOPRINTED by MALLOY LITHOGRAPHING, INC.
ANN ARBOR, MICHIGAN

# FOREWORD

Because of the immensity and complexity of the field of botany, the great diversity of plants, and the many methods of plant study, the problem of how to present to the student the highlights of botanical knowledge gained over centuries is not easy to solve. The authors and editors of the volumes in this series believe that an understanding of plants—their parts, their activities, and their relationship to man—is of fundamental importance in appreciating the significance of life. To stress this concept, the form and function of plants, tissues, and cells are treated together. At all levels of organization, in each volume, information gathered by morphologists, physiologists, cytologists, taxonomists, geneticists, biochemists, and ecologists is combined.

Thus, in the volume on *The Plant Cell* by William A. Jensen, the structure and function of the various cell parts are discussed together —for example, mitochondria and respiration, photosynthesis and chloroplasts. The volume by Stanton A. Cook, *Reproduction, Heredity, and Sexuality,* combines the principles of genetics with the means of reproduction in the various plant groups. *Nonvascular Plants: Form and Function,* by William T. Doyle, and *Vascular Plants: Form and Function,* by Frank B. Salisbury and Robert V. Parke, cover the major plant groups and discuss the plants in terms of morphology, physiology, and biochemistry. The relation of plants, particularly vascular plants, to their environment and to each other is covered in *Plants and the Ecosystem* by W. D. Billings. The form and distribution of plants of the past and their relation to the concepts of evolution are considered by Harlan Banks in *Evolution and Plants of the Past.* Herbert G. Baker, in *Plants and Civilization,* discusses the importance of plants to man's social and economic development and the equally important consideration of man's role in the modification and distribution of plants.

In a series such as this, the editors are faced with the task of dividing a broad field into areas that can be presented in a meaningful way by the authors. There must be logic in the entire scheme, with few gaps and a minimum of overlap. Yet an instructor may not want to use the series of volumes in the sequence and manner preferred by the editors. Consequently, each volume must be usable alone and also in any sequence with the others. To achieve such a high degree of versatility is difficult, but we believe the series exhibits these features.

A concerted effort has been made by the authors and editors to maintain a consistent level of presentation. However, each author has been encouraged to approach his subject in his own way and to write in his own style in order to provide variety and to exploit the uniqueness of the individual author's viewpoint. Finally, while presenting the principles of botany we have tried to communicate the excitement of recent developments as well as the joy that comes with the extension of knowledge in any field.

This book is an elementary introduction to ecology. Emphasis is given to the relationships of plant individuals and populations to their environments and to their roles in ecosystems. The text is directed to the reader who knows little or nothing about ecology. He should finish his reading with a better appreciation of the intricacy and delicacy of the relationships between organisms and their environments, and he should also realize the urgency of understanding the functioning of ecosystems, those complex natural machines upon which we all depend.

# CONTENTS

# 1

# WHAT

# IS

# ECOLOGY?

Ecology is the attempt to understand the relationship of plants and animals to their environments—where they live, how they live there, and, hopefully, why they live there. An environment is the sum of all external forces or influences (for example, heat) that affect the life of an organism. Each of us has an environmental history different from that of anyone else. Your own environment changes continually in space and time, and has done so all through your life. At this very moment you are the product of your total environmental history as it has affected the action of your inherited genetic code. Similarly, every plant has a unique and continually changing environment, although, since plants are fixed in one spot, their environments change principally in time.

An ecologist is an integrator as well as an observer and experimenter. He brings together data from many sources—genetics, taxonomy, physiology, soil science, climatology, geology, physics, and chemistry—in order to try to explain the behavior of an organism or organic community in nature. If data are lacking about a particular subject, the ecologist must get information by measurement or experiment. Since the typical ecological problem involves analysis as well as integration, an ecologist should be broadly trained in all the sciences so that he can obtain and evaluate data from whatever source and from them synthesize working models of *ecological systems*. An ecological system consists of a central biological component of one or more organisms and the environment with which the organisms interact and from which they receive energy.

## LEVELS OF INTEGRATION

There are three main levels of integration in ecology—that is, three principal kinds of ecological systems:

1. The individual
2. The population
3. The ecosystem

Each system, unlike a species or a genus, is not a hypothetical construct but a concrete reality, and its structure and interactions can be observed and measured. The complexity of structure and operation of these systems increases manyfold from the individual to the population, and almost astronomically from the population to the ecosystem. Let's look more closely at each of these systems.

**The Individual.** The individual plant or animal is a genetically uniform entity; normally, no subdivision or part can live independent of the rest of the organism for more than a short time. The individual and its accompanying environment make up an *individual ecological system.*

Most organisms are individuals and are distinct from their fellows. However, many plants (e.g., Bermuda grass, strawberries) have vegetative parts such as rhizomes or runners, which can produce new plants that remain attached to the parent plant and that are genetically identical to it. With such plants, which reproduce vegetatively, it is often difficult to decide just what is an individual and what is a small population, or clone, of genetically identical individuals all somewhat connected by vascular tissues.

The ecology of the individual is concerned with the way that particular plant (or animal) interacts with its environment. It is well to think of this individual organism-environment complex as a system that changes somewhat over a period of time. The environmental part of the system supplies the energy and raw materials that the organic part of the system (the individual) uses in living and in the production of new protoplasm. This level of integration may be called "physiological ecology."

**The Population.** An individual plant (or animal) is related to other organisms in two ways: (a) *genetically* to other members of its species, and (b) *ecologically* to other plants and animals of its biological community.

Any relatively isolated, interbreeding group of individuals is called a *local population*. Because of the gene exchange and the continuity of the population through time, the local population rather than the individual is the basic unit in evolution. The genetic structure of each local population in a species is often somewhat different from that of any other local population in the same species. This is so because, through natural selection, individuals with genes that allow them to be particularly well fitted to that local environment tend to survive in greater numbers than individuals not so well adapted.

One of the ways in which a local population can become adapted to a certain place is by developing and maintaining, by sexual reproduction, some genetic diversity within the population. This results in an array of individuals each with slightly different environmental tolerances, some of which may be better able to tolerate extreme environmental conditions than the average member of the population. This heterogeneous population structure provides the population with a kind of genetic insurance against environmental disasters, such as an unusually bitter winter or a prolonged drought. It is also advantageous in the continual adjustments of the population to the slower changes in climate that take place over hundreds or thousands of years.

Homogeneity of genetic structure can be an all or nothing proposition when it comes to a question of a species surviving environmental extremes. The safer but less efficient way is genetic heterogeneity. It is well to remember, also, that the environmental history of an individual or population is also involved in survival.

A local population in a specific environment tends by natural selection to become genetically adapted to that environment by the survival of individuals with certain genes or gene combinations. Since in non-mountainous country the climate may be generally the same over a considerable area, the local populations of a given species within this area tend to develop similar environmental tolerances and to be relatively distinct from the rest of the species. Such a group of local populations is called an *ecological race*. For example, Göte Turesson of Sweden found that in Scandinavia several species of widely distributed plants consist of ecological races. Several of these species, even though unrelated, exhibit similar or parallel adaptations to environment in their ecological races; for example, the plants on mountain tops are dwarfed and early flowering, whereas the plants on coastal rocks are sprawling and late flowering. All the local populations of each species in each place had these respective characteristics in most individuals. One might at first think that the unusually small size of these plants is only the result of the severe environments in each place, that if they were removed to a quiet garden they would grow up into strong, healthy, erect plants. Turesson tried just that, but the dwarfed or sprawling, early flowering or late flowering characteristics continued, indicating that the differences are genetic, selected over many generations by the environment. Each group of populations is made up of plants genetically adapted to the particular environmental type, alpine or coastal. The same kind of thing occurs in many North

American plants, such as California coastal and mountain species, prairie grasses, and plants of the arctic and alpine tundras.

It is now believed that many, though not all, widely distributed species of plants are made up of ecological races which in turn consist of a number of local populations made up of individuals. If environmental gradients are gradual across an area, genetic adaptation also tends to be gradual, and sharp distinctions between ecological races may not exist. The series of plants showing this gradual but continuous shift in genetically determined environmental tolerance is called an *ecocline*. Some species are made up of easily delineated ecological races; other species consist of complex ecoclines.

We can approach the study of the ecology of populations from at least two different viewpoints. First, we can study the growth of single populations, or the interactions between closely related or unrelated populations, in controlled or uncontrolled environments. In such cases, we are, in reality, studying in detail a small piece of an ecosystem. This approach has been called "population ecology." Second, we can study one or more local populations of a single species in an attempt to learn something of the species' genetically determined tolerance to environmental conditions. This approach has been termed "genecology" or perhaps "comparative physiological ecology."

**The Ecosystem.** Individuals and populations do not live alone in nature but in association with at least a few, and usually a great many, other plants and animals. These aggregations of organisms are not haphazard accumulations; on the contrary, they are spatially ordered, machine-like organizations which utilize energy and raw materials in their operation. Such a machine-like community of plants and animals, together with the environment that controls it, is called an *ecosystem*. An ecosystem represents the highest level of integration in ecological systems; it consists of many individual systems and population systems. Since no matter what their genetic ties, individuals and populations exist and operate as parts of ecosystems, the basic unit of ecology is the ecosystem. Physiological ecology, population ecology, and genecology give valuable information in helping us to construct a model of any particular ecosystem type; but ecology in its broadest sense is the study of ecosystems—their structure and operation.

Ecosystems can be of any size from a jar of water containing algae and protozoa in the laboratory window to the great Amazonian rain forest—and even the earth itself. Whatever the size, an ecosystem operates as a whole unit; both its physical and biological parts are so enmeshed in their functions that it is difficult to describe the system by neat, separate categories classified according to the roles these parts play in the machine. Indeed, all of the organisms play at least two roles: as parts of the living core of the system, and as parts of the environment itself. Nevertheless, if we are to understand ecosystems, we must attempt to analyze their structure and the functions of their various components. It is well to remember, however, that there are not always sharp lines delimiting the roles of each component, and that even apparently sharp boundaries may shift with the seasons or over long periods of time.

We may begin by recalling that an ecosystem is made up of two large parts: the physical environment and the biological community. Within the biological community, biological environmental components are added to the physical ones. However, the environment itself, including both its physical and biological parts, acts as a whole, and the subdivision above is made mainly to differentiate between the origins of the environmental factors. In the ecosystem, the physical environment provides the energy, raw materials, and living space that the biological community needs and uses for growth and maintenance.

The biological part of the system usually consists of four or five energy levels. These *trophic levels* are based on how far the original energy has come through the community. In the following outline, trophic level 1 is indicated as $T_1$, trophic level 2 as $T_2$, and so on.

$T_1$ is the green vegetation. This is the part of the community that captures and stores solar energy in photosynthesis and releases oxygen. The rest of the community is completely dependent upon this level. It is often called the "producer" level.

$T_2$ consists of the *herbivores,* which range in size from certain plant-parasitic fungi to elephants, and which digest plant material from $T_1$ and derive their energy from this plant food.

$T_3$ and $T_4$ consist of *carnivores,* animals that get their energy by eating herbivores; the energy is thus one more step removed from its original source. The animals at $T_4$ get at least some of their energy by eating carnivores at $T_3$. Although one might think of typical carnivores as being tigers or mountain lions, there are many other carnivores, ranging from insects and spiders to birds and lizards, weasels and shrews. Some organisms such as bears and man are difficult to pigeonhole as $T_2$ or $T_3$ because they are *omnivores,* sometimes eating plant material and sometimes eating other animals.

$T_5$ includes fungi, bacteria, some protozoa, and other small organisms that use dead plant and animal material as food. These *decomposers* break down organic structures and substances, releasing compounds and elements back into the environment and also utilizing energy and carrying it another step or several steps beyond its capture. Although for simplicity we lump all these decomposers into one trophic level, the situation is far more complex. There are fungi that live on fungi, bacteria that live on fungi, viruses that live on bacteria, and so on—and all of them in a sense are decomposers. Trophic level 5 is really a collection of several different trophic levels all utilizing energy, with the "top" decomposers finally releasing the last of the energy back to the environment. The various members of this decomposer level also utilize dead plant or animal material or wastes from all of the lower trophic levels.

In terrestrial ecosystems, most of the decomposers live on the surface or in the upper part of the soil, converting dead material into humus and eventually into minerals, gases, and water. The importance of the decomposers is obvious; without them dead material would simply accumulate and raw materials in short supply, such as phosphorus, would be tied up in the remains of plants and animals. The decomposers provide the necessary cycling mechanism in the ecosystem. Energy simply flows in one end of an ecosystem (at photosynthesis) and flows out (by respiration) everywhere along the line. But because of decomposers, all elemental materials cycle, at least to some extent, within the system and between systems.

At the level of the individual, at the level of the population, and even at the level of the vegetation, it is possible to speak of plant ecology and animal ecology. But the interactions of the ecosystem involve all kinds of organisms in a complex community whose understanding requires a broader viewpoint, that of ecology itself.

# 2

# THE

# ENVIRONMENT

An environment occupies three-dimensional space and extends through time. But this does not mean that the environment is uniform throughout its space or through time. On the contrary, natural environments almost always show vertical and lateral gradients in their spatial dimension, and in their time dimension they reflect the strong diurnal and annual cycles of solar radiation. In addition to these cyclic effects, some environments show slow or rapid cumulative (noncyclic) changes, such as erosion of land surfaces and silting of ponds and lakes. Space and time, then, are best considered as dimensions of an environment rather than as factors or components.

Suppose we consider the environment of a tall redwood tree (*Sequoia sempervirens*) on the foggy northern California coast. Within the three-dimensional volume of the tree's environment, there are strong vertical gradients of light, temperature, fog, and other components. There is a rather sharp discontinuity in these vertical gradients at the surface of the soil. For example, the soil temperature is often quite different from air temperature and may increase or decrease with depth depending upon the time of year. Similar but shallower environmental gradients also exist laterally. In any case, it is very difficult to define precisely the spatial limits of the tree's environment; flow of energy (radiation, heat), atmosphere, water, and nutrients into and out of the immediate environment may be dependent upon events and conditions at some distance away. Thus, these distant events and sources also constitute a part of the total environment of the tree, although they do not fit into the comparatively precise three-dimensional volume of the immediate environment. Necessary minerals such as calcium and phosphate are in the soil close to the roots. But the light that drives photosynthesis comes from the sun, 93 million miles across space. Even so, since it takes light only about 8 minutes to reach the tree from the sun, the light may reach the leaves 300 feet above the ground well before a phosphate ion starting from the soil at the same time would reach them. Consequently, the distant sun is just as much a part of the immediate environment as is the phosphate mineral in the soil. The environment of the redwood occupies three-dimensional space but with poorly defined boundaries. The tree's environment also has a certain continuity through time, even though night alternates with day, winter follows summer, and the tree itself grows taller and adds new environmental space year by year.

## ENVIRONMENTAL COMPONENTS

An environment is a complex of many factors that interact not only with the organism but among themselves. As a result, it is difficult to isolate one part of the environment and change it without affecting other parts of the environment. Nevertheless, if we are to understand the structure and operation of an environment, we must subdivide it, at least in an abstract way, in order to know what to measure and what to study.

Some ecologists divide the environment into two parts: the *physical environment* and the *biological environment.* In a way, this is rather artificial, since the environment acts as a single complex system, and the effects of other organisms in the environment usually are felt through the physical factors. For example, the effect of a tall spruce tree on the spruce seedlings growing under it is mainly expressed in cutting down the amount of light. The diagram in Fig. 2-1 shows some of the complex interactions that take place between the plant and the principal components of its environment. Notice how indirect the effects of many factors can be.

At any given time, environments differ in both the absolute and relative amounts of these factors. They also differ in the rates of flow of certain factors through the environment—for example, of heat and water. We should remember that environments are dynamic—that is, they change through time (cyclically or cumulatively) and there is inflow and outflow of certain components. The result is that gradients, strong or weak, exist in every natural environment through space and time. It is not enough to measure the amounts of the principal components at a given point at a given instant in time. We need to know both the spatial and temporal gradients and flow rates for the important environmental factors.

In a small ravine, the amount of solar radiation received in winter will show a steep horizontal gradient from the shaded slope to the sunny slope. This will result in soil and lower air temperatures having

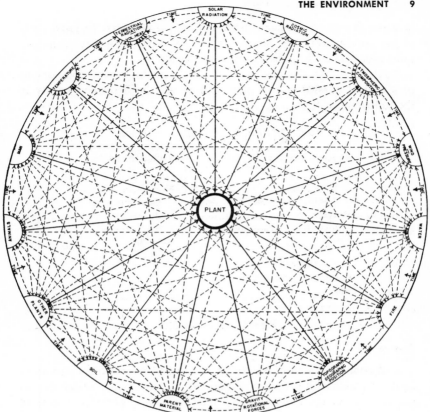

**Fig. 2-1.** *Diagrammatic representation of the complex and holo-coenotic interactions between environmental factors and an organism. Solid lines show factor-plant relationships; dashed lines show factor interactions. Time is an environmental dimension, not a factor, and its modifying influence is indicated by inward-pointing arrows just inside the border of the diagram. Diagram from Billings (1952).*

similar gradients across the ravine. On the warmer slope, there will also be a steep vertical air temperature gradient on a sunny winter day. This is because the air very close to the soil absorbs heat from the soil while the upper air stays cold. Temperature on this same slope will also show a steep gradient through time when night replaces day and the heat income stops while heat loss continues. The environment in the ravine, therefore, even in temperature alone, is dynamic. The distribution and growth of organisms in the ravine reflects these differences; the sunny slope will be populated with heat-requiring and drought-resistant forms which start to grow early in the spring, while the shady slopes will have those organisms requiring less heat, less light, and more water.

Table 2-1 lists the principal physical and biological components of a typical natural environment. These will be described briefly in the following section.

**Table 2-1.** *Environmental Components*

| Physical Factors | Biological Factors |
| --- | --- |
| Energy | Green plants |
|   Radiation | Non-green plants |
|   Temperature and heat flow |   Decomposers |
| Water |   Parasites |
| Atmospheric gases and wind |   Symbionts |
| Fire | Animals |
| Gravity | Man |
| Topography | |
| Geologic substratum | |
| Soil | |

## PHYSICAL FACTORS

### Energy

**Radiation.** Radiation is energy moving at or near the speed of light. Practically all of the energy in an ecosystem originates as radiation from the sun—that is, *solar radiation*. Minor amounts of high energy cosmic radiation coming from beyond the solar system also enter our environments and, though they do not contribute much to energy flow through the ecosystem, are of considerable biological significance because of their ionizing effects on chromosome structure. Similar high energy radiation is received in certain local environments due to the presence of radioactive rocks or fallout. Around volcanoes and hot springs, some geothermal energy (heat) of nonsolar origin is added to local environments. But all of these latter sources are relatively minor; it is solar radiation that provides the necessary energy to heat the environment and to drive the ecosystem by means of energy storage at photosynthesis.

Solar radiation as received at the earth's surface consists mostly of visible radiation or light, infrared or thermal radiation, and ultraviolet radiation—the relative quantities being in that order. In addition, solar X rays and high energy solar particles (electrons and protons) are received in the upper atmosphere. The X rays are absorbed by the high altitude atmospheric gases, as are most of the ultraviolet rays. Most of the charged particles are trapped in the Van Allen radiation belts at some distance above the earth.

*Light* is that radiation with wavelengths between 400–760 millimicrons, violet at the shorter end of the wavelength span and red at the longer end. It is visible to our eyes whereas other radiation is not. Light is also the effective radiation in photosynthesis and is important to a considerable extent in the heating of the environment. Light makes up almost half of the solar radiation reaching the earth's surface.

Most of the remainder of solar radiation is *infrared* or *thermal radiation,* consisting of wavelengths over 760 millimicrons. It is invisible to the human eye but can be felt as radiant heat. A relatively small portion of solar radiation is *ultraviolet,* with wavelengths shorter than visible light. All solar radiation is depleted as it passes through the atmosphere by atmospheric absorption and scattering. However, this depletion is most striking and of greatest biological importance in the ultraviolet. Much of the solar ultraviolet is absorbed by the ozone layer of the upper atmosphere about 16 miles up. Because of the detrimental effects of ultraviolet on cells, this is a fortunate thing for life on earth. Even at 14,000 feet, as on the top of Mount Evans in Colorado, there is about twice as much ultraviolet as at sea level. It may be cold on a bright summer day on such a mountain top, but because of the high amount of ultraviolet one can get a sunburn very quickly—even more quickly if there are reflecting snowbanks present. High energy radiation of cosmic origin is also more intense on mountain summits. With higher amounts of all kinds of radiation, alpine locations present a rather extreme and somewhat severe radiation environment with pronounced biological effects.

Since solar radiation provides the energy for photosynthesis and also is the source of environmental heat, we must know how different environments compare in the amounts of such radiation received. Three things must be known: (1) the intensity or amount per unit area per unit time; (2) the quality or wavelength composition; and (3) photoperiod or duration.

While intensity can be measured by photoelectric light meters in terms of illumination units such as foot-candles, it is better measured in energy units such as (1) ergs per square centimeter per second or (2) langleys. One langley is equal to one gram calorie per square centimeter. The rate of energy inflow at sea level at noon in clear summer weather is usually around 1.3 to 1.4 langleys per minute. On high mountains, however, the rate of energy inflow may be as high at 1.6 to 1.8 langleys per minute. At the outer edge of the earth's atmosphere, the figure is about 2 langleys per minute—the so-called "solar constant." Thus, the atmosphere absorbs some solar radiation. The atmosphere, in turn, radiates this energy as long wavelengths, some of which reach the earth's surface. The noon figures of 1.3 to 1.8 langleys per minute include some of this thermal radiation coming down from the atmosphere.

Instruments used to measure radiation in terms of energy units are very important in studying the *energy budget* of an environment. They are of several types and are called radiometers or pyrheliometers. Instruments such as these can determine the total number of langleys received per day at different times of the year at different latitudes and altitudes. Other instruments known as net radiometers indicate the balance between this incoming radiation and outgoing thermal radiation from soil or vegetational surfaces. From these net radiometers, we can get some idea of the net amount of energy available to heat the air and soil, evaporate water, and run photosynthesis in different kinds of ecosystems.

**Temperature and Heat Flow.** Radiant energy may be absorbed by the molecules of gases, liquids, or solids. Such absorption of energy raises the temperature of the absorbing substance. If temperature differences exist in the environment, the energy will then flow as heat from the warmer substance to colder substances or regions. This flow may be by molecular conduction, by mass movement (air or water currents), or by reradiation at longer wavelengths. Energy may also be carried away as latent heat by evaporation. All of these processes result in a drop in temperature of the substance or body that is losing heat. Temperature, then, is a measure of the tendency of a substance to give up heat. Heat flows from warm substances (higher temperatures) to colder substances (lower temperatures).

Two aspects of temperature are important in the environment and in the organism. First, the *absolute temperature* governs the speed of biological processes and physical reactions. The absolute temperature of a body or surface also determines its heat loss by radiation; this radiational heat loss is proportional to the fourth power of the absolute temperature of the body. Secondly, the *relative temperatures* of organisms and different parts of the environment indicate the direction and rate of heat flow by other processes such as conduction. Both absolute and relative temperatures may be determined by suitably scaled thermometers, either small or large, recording or nonrecording.

Since solar radiation and temperature both have daily and yearly cycles, heat is far from static in most environments. There is a continual flow of heat between different parts of the environment and between the environment and the organism, first in one direction and then in the other. In order to understand energy relationships in the environment and in the ecosystem, we must know a great deal about these heat transfer processes. This, of course, means that we must know relative and absolute temperatures of organisms and environmental components not just at a given instant but continuously through the daily and annual cycles.

Since the ultimate source of most environmental heat is solar radiation, we might expect to find the highest temperatures in environments with the greatest amounts of solar radiation. This is so up to a point. In the tropics, for example, where solar radiation is high throughout the year, temperature is also high throughout the year. This is particularly true of tropical deserts, where there is little cloud cover to interfere with solar radiation. This very lack of cloud cover also results in strong outgoing thermal radiation, so that nights tend to be relatively cool and there is considerable daily amplitude in the temperature cycle. There is greater uniformity in the warm temperatures of the tropical rain-forest regions, where clouds prevent both daytime and nighttime temperatures from reaching the extremes found under desert conditions.

Environments with the lowest temperatures are in polar regions and in alpine regions along the summits of high mountains. These environments have periods during the summer when amounts of solar radiation are high. But more than counterbalancing this periodic high solar radiation are long dark periods in the winter, low angles at which the sun's rays are received, much reflecting snow to be melted, and, in the case of alpine areas, thin atmosphere that does not absorb much radiation either from the earth or from the sun. Taking the year as a whole, solar-radiation totals reaching dry soil surfaces in such places are not great. The little heat that is absorbed is readily reradiated into the thin mountain air or into the clear night sky. Hence, temperatures drop to extremely low levels and stay there for months at a time during the period of low sun.

Air does not absorb a great deal of solar radiation directly. The temperature of the lower air increases primarily by the absorption of long-wave thermal radiation from the heated soil, and by convection and conduction of heat from this warm soil surface. Compare, for example, the hot lower air temperatures over dry desert rocks and sand with the cold temperatures over melting snow—both on bright sunny days.

Because of the density and low specific heat of dry soil, soil temperature rises rapidly in sunlight. The higher the temperature of the soil surface, the more it tends to lose heat by radiation, conduction, or convection to the lower air. The temperature of water rises more slowly than that of soil or rock, but water holds the heat longer. Because of transparency and mixing, heat tends to be distributed rather rapidly throughout a considerable depth of water. On the other hand, heat moves relatively slowly down into soil because it can move only by conduction. The result is a rather steep temperature gradient in soils from the surface to the depth of 30 centimeters or so under dry and sunny conditions. The surface has a relatively high temperature during the day but is somewhat colder at night as heat flows into and out of the soil. This diurnal temperature difference at the surface of desert soils may be as much as 100°F. The daily heat-flow wave does not penetrate farther than about 30 centimeters but the annual heat wave may go down much farther—as much as several meters in warm climates.

The data in Fig. 2-2 show the strong daily cycling of temperature in the lower air and upper soil and the lack of such diurnal cycling in the temperature of the subsoil. However, the subsoil temperature shows a long, gradual annual cycle, being warmest in early autumn and coldest in late winter or early spring.

In addition to daily and annual temperature cycles, there are vertical and horizontal temperature gradients. In places where solar radiation reaches most of the ground surface, daytime air temperature increases downward to a maximal air temperature just above the soil surface. At the same time, of course, soil temperature is highest at the surface, which is usually somewhat higher in temperature than the air immediately above it. In such a location the temperature gradients at night are usually reversed; the lowest air temperature and the lowest soil temperature are both very close to the soil surface. From the standpoint of the tolerance of seedlings to temperature, it is easy to see that this shallow layer of air very close to the soil surface may have critically high or low temperatures with resultant death or damage to the plant. The first freezing temperatures in the autumn and the last in spring are often confined to just this shallow layer on clear, windless nights. The thicker the vegetational cover, the less marked is this temperature layer near the soil surface. Bright, warm days and clear nights in early spring result in strong daily cycling of lower air temperatures in the leafless deciduous forest of the eastern United States. On the other hand, there is little diurnal variation in

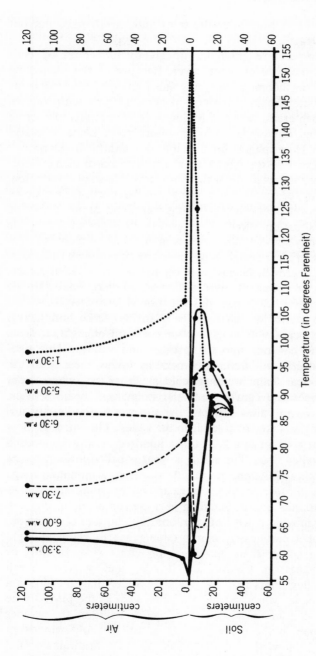

**Fig. 2-2.** The daily cycle of lower air and soil temperatures as shown by temperature profiles at selected times of the day. Note the severity of the soil surface environment as indicated by its low and high extremes as compared with the relative lack of daily variation below 30 centimeters where only an annual cycle exists. Data from a vegetated sandy area in the Nevada desert (31 July 1953) with clear weather.

Temperature (in degrees Farenheit)

Air

Soil

centimeters

centimeters

1:30 P.M.

5:30 P.M.

6:30 P.M.

7:30 A.M.

6:00 A.M.

3:30 A.M.

15

these temperatures in May after the trees and shrubs have put out their canopy of leaves.

Horizontal temperature gradients are greatly influenced by both topography and the type of plant cover. Because of the blanketing effect of foliage on incoming and outgoing radiation, forested areas have lower daytime temperatures and higher nighttime temperatures than adjacent open areas. Areas of rolling or broken topography often show considerable differences in temperature from place to place. In the Northern Hemisphere, for example, a south-facing slope will generally be warmer in the winter than a nearby north-facing slope, which because of the low angle of the sun receives less solar radiation. Often, there may be much snow lying on the north-facing slope, whereas the opposite south-facing slope is warm and sunny. This type of temperature situation allows plant growth to begin earlier in the spring on the sunny slope. It also permits many kinds of plants to exist far to the north of their usual range on warm south-facing hillsides. Conversely, plant growth begins later on the colder, shaded slopes, where northern or boreal plants reach their southern limits. In the Southern Hemisphere, of course, this situation is just reversed.

Compared to warm air, cold air is relatively dense and heavy. Because of this increase in weight as air cools off at night, it flows down slopes and canyons into depressions and valleys. This phenomenon, called *cold-air drainage,* works as follows: Early in the evening during clear, calm weather, cold air from the upper slopes flows down ravines and canyons into the valley and, being heavier, runs under the warm valley air, pushing the warm air directly upward and forming a "lake" of cold air in the valley. The warm air now lies on top of the cold air at a height of a hundred or several hundred feet above the valley floor. The result is what is called a *temperature inversion.* In such a situation, the middle slopes of a mountain range are often much warmer at night in clear weather than the valleys below or the summits above. Standing in a canyon at night, one can feel the cold air moving down from upslope. The bottom of a canyon, therefore, is not a particularly comfortable place to camp at night since it is often colder than the slopes on either side. In hilly or mountainous places in California, Nevada, and western North Carolina, the valley floors may be 10–20°F colder than the slopes a thousand feet above. Many species of plants, such as the pinyon pine (*Pinus monophylla*) in Nevada, are restricted to living on the warmer slopes rather than in the colder valleys or on the cold windswept crests above. A knowledge of the effects of cold-air drainage and temperature inversions is of great practical significance in the growing of tender plants and in locating orange groves, peach orchards, and other crops susceptible to frost.

Plants differ in their metabolic response to temperature and in their tolerance to extreme temperatures. There is considerable difference in temperature tolerance not only from species to species but also within the same plant from time to time within the year. In general, there is little metabolic activity at temperatures below 0°C (32°F) or higher than 45°C (113°F). However, some extremely hardy arctic and alpine plants do carry on photosynthesis at temperatures below freezing, and a number of plants are active at temperatures above 40°C (104°F). Many plants are killed by freezing temperatures as high as 0°C, and many tropical plants are killed by chilling at even higher temperatures. Some arctic-alpine plants die even at moderately warm temperatures, while almost all seed plants become inactive or are killed after prolonged exposure to temperatures above 55°C (131°F). On the other hand, a few kinds of blue-green algae can tolerate temperatures in hot springs above 70°C (158°F), and die or become inactive at temperatures below 55°C.

Plants, unlike warm-blooded animals, are at the mercy of the environment in regard to temperature. Plant temperatures are the result of a complex of processes in which heat is exchanged with the environment. Except in sunlight of high intensity, temperatures of leaves, stems, flowers, and fruits are usually very close to ambient air temperature. However, in bright sunlight, plant temperatures may be 10–20°C above the temperature of the surrounding air, although when a shadow passes between the plant and the direct rays of the sun, the plant temperature quickly drops to or even below that of the air.

A plant can gain heat in several ways. Principally this gain is by absorption of radiation, conduction from the thin air or water layer immediately over the surface of the leaf or stem, and by respiration. It can lose heat by conduction and convection to the surrounding medium, by radiation of long wavelengths, or as latent heat by the evaporation and transpiration of water. All leaves also reflect some light and infrared energy before such radiant energy can enter the heat economy of the leaf. In the final analysis, an ordinary leaf is a fairly efficient gatherer of light energy by photosynthesis, and at the same time rather efficient at keeping leaf temperatures down to a reasonable level by losing heat in transpiration, conduction, convection, and radiation.

The best measure of inflow and outflow of heat in an environment is provided by determining the heat or energy budget. The energy budget is an excellent integrator of physical environmental conditions; but, since it involves some things we have not yet explained, it will be discussed later in the chapter.

## Water

Since all life requires water and since water is unevenly distributed over the earth, its abundance or scarcity in an environment is reflected in striking vegetational characteristics. Luxuriant temperate rain forests, dripping with water and moss, occur along the coasts and seaward mountains of the state of Washington. Yet scarcely 100 miles to the east, across the Cascade Mountains, dry sagebrush bakes in the desert sun. Why is this? The answer is partly physical and partly biological. The environments are decidedly different in the two regions because of differences in precipitation and solar radiation. The vegetations themselves are different because of the sorting effect of water and drought on the various kinds of gene systems in the available flora.

The amount of water in the earth's atmosphere is quite limited but very mobile, and circulates continuously from air to land and sea and back to the atmosphere again. According to R. C. Sutcliffe, a British meteorologist, the earth's atmosphere at any one time contains the equivalent of only about one inch of rainfall. Considering the earth as a whole, this is just about 10 days' supply. Since worldwide droughts do not occur, cycling of this water through precipitation, stream flow, transpiration, and evaporation must be continual and relatively rapid. This circulation, called the *hydrologic cycle* (or water cycle), is diagrammed in Fig. 2-3.

Even though on an average worldwide basis the cycle has a relatively rapid turnover, it is far from being uniform in rate both in space and time. Some parts of the earth receive hundreds of inches of precipitation a year, whereas others such as the northern Chilean coast are almost rainless. In many places, the cycle changes seasonally through the year, with dry seasons regularly following wet seasons. In California, for example, the summer is always very dry and most rain falls during the cool season. On the plains of northern India, on the other hand, summer is the wet season when the monsoon rains follow the drought of spring. In each place, the period of vegetational growth and flowering of the native vegetation is nicely adjusted to these seasonal rainy and drought periods. Climatic records of the last hundred years, study of tree-ring patterns, and investigation of advances and retreats of glaciers all indicate that longer wet and dry cycles also exist. Some of these are as short as a few years; others are measured in terms of thousands of years.

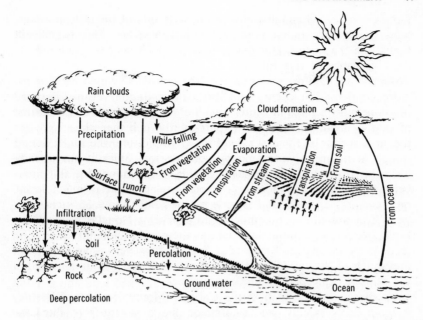

**Fig. 2-3.** *Diagrammatic representation of the hydrologic cycle. Adapted from* Water—The Yearbook of Agriculture (1955); *courtesy U.S. Department of Agriculture.*

Some of the water that falls as rain or snow on the continents originates by condensation of water vapor, which enters the atmosphere by evaporation from land surfaces or by transpiration from vegetation. However, most precipitable water vapor in the air over the continents is derived directly from the surface of the sea by evaporation. This water vapor is carried over the coastlines in masses of air moving from sea to land in the general atmospheric circulation. Upon rising over the land either by convection or due to hills or mountains, the air cools by expansion and the water vapor condenses into cloud droplets. If the droplets get large enough, they are precipitated as rain.

In the state of Washington, the source of most of the water vapor is the Pacific Ocean. This water vapor is carried shoreward by winds circulating around low pressure storm centers moving southeastward from the Aleutian Islands or Gulf of Alaska mainly during the cooler part of the year. As this maritime air hits the coastal mountain ranges, it is forced to rise. As it rises, it cools by expansion and the water vapor condenses into cloud droplets, which build up into raindrops. This results in heavy rainfall on the seaward sides of these mountains.

For example, at Quinault Lake on the west side of the coastal mountains, the average annual precipitation is 135 inches. The magnificent forest of Sitka spruce, Douglas fir, and hemlock near the lake reflects the abundance of this rainfall.

As the air continues to rise over the coastal Olympic Mountains, more condensation occurs and more precipitation results. Because of lower temperatures in winter, much of the precipitation at that time of year is in the form of snow, particularly at higher elevations. As the air descends on the east side of the Olympics into the Puget Sound trough, it naturally warms up by compression. Since it has already lost some of its moisture on the west side of the mountains and since, being warmer, it can now hold more, precipitation is much lower on the shores of the Sound. Seattle receives only about 35 inches per year. This amount is still sufficient to support a Douglas fir–hemlock forest even though not as luxuriant as the one at Quinault Lake. The mere presence of this forest near Seattle, however, is an indication that much of the rainfall at Quinault runs off into the streams and is not utilized or needed by the vegetation.

As the air moves up over the Cascade Mountains east of Seattle, it again cools rapidly, and rainfall on the west slopes of the Cascades is heavy. However, since the air is now dryer than it was over the ocean, the precipitation is not quite as heavy as at Quinault. In the Cascades, it ranges from about 80 to 100 inches per year at elevations of around 2,000 feet. Much of this, of course, is in the form of snowfall at this and higher elevations. As the air crosses the Cascade crest, it has already lost much of its water vapor. As it descends and warms on the east side, clouds evaporate easily, little or no precipitation falls, and the air becomes so dry that it is very evaporative. Because of this, the valley of the Columbia River is a desert, with annual rainfall averaging 9 inches at Wenatchee in the north to only 7 inches at Kennewick in the south. The native vegetation on the dark volcanic rocks and deep silty soils is widely scattered sagebrush and tufts of drought-resistant bunch grasses. It would be difficult to find a sharper contrast with the tall, dense forests west of the mountains—and the difference is directly attributable to the differences in water available for growth.

In the preceding example, the mountains cause what is called a *rain-shadow* effect; they produce a dry region in their lee just as a tree makes a long shadow in the late afternoon sun. Lake Quinault to the west of the mountains is in front of the rain shadow and receives the downpours of rain as the air begins to rise. Kennewick, on the other hand, being behind the mountains, is in the middle of the rain shadow and gets little or no rain as the air again descends to the low altitudes, warms up, and becomes evaporative.

For the same reasons, any high mountain area receives more precipitation than adjacent lowlands. Mountains that lie across the paths of moist oceanic winds are always very wet: the mountains of Hawaii and the Philippines in the tradewind tropics; the southern slopes of the Himalayas across the Indian Ocean monsoon winds; the Smoky Mountains and Blue Ridge of North Carolina, which intercept warm, moist air from the Gulf of Mexico.

To evaluate the role of water in an environment, we must start with information on the frequency, abundance, and type of precipitation as illustrated above. However, other information is needed. We must know how much of the water brought by precipitation actually gets into the vegetation and is metabolically involved with the protoplasm, and at what rate it is lost by transpiration and replaced from the soil by absorption. In other words, we must know the effectiveness of the precipitation in supplying an available source of soil moisture and how effective the vegetation is in utilizing and conserving this moisture.

Not all of the precipitation that falls on an area becomes available to plants as soil moisture. Depending upon the rate and kind of precipitation and also on the nature of the vegetation, a portion is intercepted by the leaves and branches. Much of this is evaporated and does not reach the soil. Some water drips from the twigs and leaves and a considerable amount runs down the trunks and stems. In open vegetation, most of the precipitation actually reaches the ground as "direct throughfall," whereas in dense coniferous forests, heavy rains may result in considerable "indirect throughfall" by way of "leaf drip" and "stem flow." Light rains of short duration may be almost completely intercepted and the water evaporated without reaching the soil surface.

Once on the soil surface, the water may run off into the streams or arroyos, or it may infiltrate into the soil. The ratio between runoff and infiltration depends upon many things: the rate and type of precipitation; the degree of vegetational interception; the porosity or compaction of the soil; the amount of leaf litter and humus on and in the surface soil; whether or not the soil is frozen; the amount of water already in the soil; and the steepness of slope. A hilly, rocky desert area will not be able to hold back a brief heavy rain or cloudburst; much of it will run off as a flash flood and the soil may not be wetted at depths of more than 2 or 3 inches. On the other hand, a similar rain on level ground occupied by dense forest and deep humus-rich soils will be absorbed as if by a sponge and the effect on stream flow will be negligible. In such forested regions, stream flow increases greatly only after several days of such rain or during the winter when trees may be leafless and the soil frozen.

Once water enters the soil, it moves downward slowly and brings the soil up to its maximum water-holding capacity before responding to gravity and moving farther down. The *water-holding capacity* (or field capacity) of a soil is a measure of its ability to hold water against the pull of gravity. This capacity is determined by the size and arrangement of the soil particles and the amount of organic matter or humus present. The forces involved are (1) *capillary,* in which surface tension of water in thin films or small spaces is involved; and (2) *hygroscopic,* in which particles actually absorb water. Clay soils or soils with a high humus content are able to hold more water than sandy soils with little organic matter. These soil forces are stronger than gravity until they are saturated, after which the water proceeds downward into dryer soil. This percolating water may even seep down to the *ground-water table,* some distance below the surface, where it is available as free liquid water for wells or springs.

Most plants depend upon the capillary fraction of "soil" moisture rather than upon the deeper "ground" water. There are, however, some kinds of trees and shrubs such as cottonwood, willow, mesquite, and greasewood, particularly in dry regions, whose roots penetrate to the ground-water table and utilize this free water. Such plants are called *phreatophytes* or "well plants." Since ground water often flows underground for many miles, desert phreatophytes may remain green through even long droughts if the ground water is continually replenished by rain falling in nearby mountains. In desert conditions where the ground water originates some distance away and is separated from the soil moisture near the surface by many feet of dry soil, an intriguing problem arises: how do the roots get through the barrier of apparently dry soil to the ground water?

Most plants, however, are not phreatophytes and must depend upon the capillary part of soil moisture as their immediate water source. This water enters the roots in response to differences between its diffusion pressure and the lesser diffusion pressures in the root cells. Water tensions within the plant are set up by the loss of water from the leaves due to the evaporative process of transpiration. As long as the water in the soil is abundant enough to be under less tension than that in the plant, it will move easily into the roots. It will then move up the xylem into the leaves and from the mesophyll cells diffuse outward as water vapor into the drier air. Thus, water may return to the air in the hydrologic cycle either by evaporation from open water or soil surfaces or by transpiration from foliage. In the latter case, it has been biologically effective on its trip through the plant, even though a considerable amount of transient water may be required for every gram of dry weight of growth.

The amount of capillary or available water in the soil depends upon the texture, structure, and depth of the soil, the time and amount of precipitation, and the transpirational activity and leaf area of the vegetation that utilizes the water. When the capillary water is used up in the root zone of the soil, the leaves will wilt, fall, or become dormant. If the soil drought continues, the plants will become dormant or die, depending upon their relative abilities to withstand such drought.

Plants such as water lilies or cattails, which have their roots in liquid water, are called *hydrophytes;* they cannot withstand prolonged drought. *Mesophytes* are plants that live in usually moist but not wet conditions; mesophytes vary in their abilities to withstand drought. Some can get through only a very few days; others may survive somewhat longer. Plants able to survive through weeks, months, or even years of soil drought are called *xerophytes.*

Almost all of the plants in the forest at Quinault Lake, with its 135 inches of precipitation per year and no real period of soil drought, are mesophytes. As in most rainy climates, there are *epiphytes* growing high in the trees and utilizing rainwater directly or by absorption from stem flow along the tree trunks or branches. Because of the cool climate, these epiphytes are almost all bryophytes and lichens rather than the orchid or bromeliad epiphytes of the tropical rain forest. On the other hand, xerophytes make up almost all of the sparse native vegetation in the dry Columbia Basin east of the Cascades. Xerophytes are of four principal types: (1) annuals, (2) phreatophytes, (3) succulents, and (4) true xerophytes.

*Annuals* are actually drought evaders since they get through the extended drought period in seed form; they resemble short-lived, diminutive mesophytes that live only when soil moisture is present and produce seeds before dying with the onset of severe drought. Annuals are well adapted to the most severe deserts where periods between rains may amount to several years, but they are present in all deserts.

*Phreatophytes* are also drought evaders in a way since they get through long droughts by tapping ground water that flows into the desert underground from the surrounding mountains. Greasewood (*Sarcobatus*) and willow (*Salix*) are good examples of phreatophytes in the Columbia Basin desert.

*Succulents* get through the dry period by utilizing water stored in stems or leaves. Cacti are succulents but are rare in the Columbia Basin because of the cold winters and the lack of precipitation during the warm season. Most succulents are susceptible to freezing and thus are more common in subtropical deserts such as those in Arizona.

The *true xerophytes* are represented in the Columbia Basin by shrubs such as sagebrush (*Artemisia*) and hopsage (*Grayia*). A true xerophyte must be able to get water from relatively dry soil by producing high diffusion-pressure deficits in leaf and root cells. It also must be able to conserve water by cutting down on transpiration rates in dry weather; such decrease is usually accomplished by having grayish, strongly constructed little leaves that can be dropped when soil drought becomes severe. Such plants become dormant and are able to last out even severe one- or two-year droughts. Some of the plants may die but the fittest survive to re-populate the deserts with seedlings when the rains return.

## Atmosphere and Wind

**Atmosphere.** The earth's characteristic atmosphere surrounds all terrestrial organisms even to the roots of the higher plants and the fungi and bacteria in the soil. Although it primarily consists of relatively inert nitrogen, the atmosphere supplies organisms with the necessary oxygen for respiration and with the carbon dioxide and water vapor required in photosynthesis. It is also the reservoir from which nitrogen slowly cycles via certain bacteria into the living parts of the ecosystem.

With increasing altitude, the number of molecules of any gas decreases per unit volume of atmosphere. In high mountains there is a relative scarcity of oxygen, which can sometimes result in death to low altitude life. Many human beings, animals, and plants can become adapted if they are slowly acclimated to the low atmospheric pressures and low oxygen partial pressures of the high mountains. Native life is already metabolically adjusted in one way or another.

Not so well known, but just as obvious, is the fact that carbon dioxide varies from place to place, even at sea level, and, of course, is also in short supply per volume at high altitudes, although its relative concentration remains at about 0.03 per cent. There is some evidence now that this reduced amount of carbon dioxide on high mountains may be an important factor in the environment of alpine plants.

Atmospheric pressure in itself affects man and certain animals in its altitudinal decrease. Most people have felt their ears "pop" in rapid ascents or descents in an airplane or on a mountain road. At an elevation of 12,000 feet, over one third of the atmosphere is below. Such reduced atmospheric pressure is an important characteristic of mountain environments. Little is known of the effects of reduced pressure on plants, but it does play a role in their utilization of carbon dioxide and oxygen.

**Wind.** Wind is atmosphere in motion. It serves to circulate oxygen, carbon dioxide, and water vapor. Without its effects on the hydrologic cycle, the land would be arid, though wind is also involved in evaporation and loss of water from an environment. Some of its effects are physical. The physical damage to trees in hurricanes and on mountain ridges is visible evidence of its power to determine the kinds of plants that can grow in exposed environments. Very windy places are likely to be populated by short plants growing in the protection of a rock or crevice or by pliant grasses waving in the breeze.

Wind is the principal cause of *timberline*—the line beyond which trees do not grow—in the high mountains of the Northern Hemisphere. The twisted timberline trees, or "krummholz," in Fig. 2-4 are not the result of wind pressure alone. The bark and twigs of these trees are blasted by snow and ice particles carried by the terrific winter winds at these altitudes. Only the part of the scrubby tree which

**Fig. 2-4.** *Flag-form and basal "krummholz" of wind-trimmed Engelmann spruce near timberline in the Medicine Bow Mountains, Wyoming.*

is covered by the snow pack can escape this icy blast. However, the leeward side of the tree is semiprotected by the trunk; the result is a "flag-form" individual. Similarly, the one-sided trees of the seacoast are caused by wind. But again, the role of pressure is minor; it is the droplets of salt spray carried from the surf that cause the damage to buds and leaves and allow only slow growth on the seaward side.

## Fire

Fire is not an ever present environmental factor; in environments such as the arctic tundra it almost never occurs. But fire, though it may be only minutes in actual duration, can leave marks on an environment that may take centuries to overcome.

The spruce-fir forests of the Rocky Mountains are particularly susceptible to fire in late summer, and these forests have been burned repeatedly. In the Medicine Bow Mountains of southern Wyoming there is an extensive virgin tract of old Engelmann spruce and subalpine fir that has not been burned during recorded history. The large spruce trees average from 325 to 375 years old; there is no sign of fire on their trunks. Yet one can go anywhere in this forest with a spade, dig a hole, and find charcoal. The mountains around this forest show considerable evidence of more recent fires—tangled windfalls of burned tree trunks, young lodgepole pines coming up through the debris, old fire-scarred snags of spruce still standing a century or more after they were killed. Fire has left its mark on the montane environments of western North America through the centuries, and continues to do so.

Some ecologists consider fire to be a biological rather than physical factor because modern man is the cause of so many forest and grassland fires. Although man has increased its incidence, fire has always been a part of many environments, and there is no doubt of its physical impact.

Lightning is the most important cause of natural fires. In the Rocky Mountain forests it causes hundreds of forest fires every year. Many of these would be catastrophic if it were not for the vigilance of fire fighters in the U.S. Forest Service and National Park Service. In spite of the increased incidence of man-caused fires, the protection provided by these services has undoubtedly restricted the area of forest burned annually compared to what it was a century ago when any fire could burn until it ran out of fuel or was checked by rain. Many western forests of the mid-nineteenth century were open and resembled parks with their carpets of grasses. They were kept that way by repeated ground fires, which did relatively little damage to the older trees but burned the dry grass and brush. Today, protected forests have a dense understory of young trees. When fire does come to these crowded forests in a dry year, everything burns and the environment is completely opened up by a disastrous crown fire. There were crown fires in the past too, but because of the open type of forest they were less likely to occur.

In a few minutes, fire can completely change an environment that took a thousand years of forest growth to build. On the other hand, if fire is relatively frequent in an environment, it actually may be the controlling factor in an ecosystem made up almost entirely of fire-resistant organisms. Such is the case in some of the open, longleaf-pine and wire-grass forests of the sandy coastal plain of the southeastern United States, where frequent ground fires help to maintain this vegetation type. Without fires to eliminate biological competition from other species, many kinds of pine forest (e.g., the red pine forests of northern Minnesota) would be replaced by other and perhaps less productive forests.

And yet, in general, fires (usually set by man) are slowly shrinking the forested areas of the world. Surprisingly, it is in the tropical forested areas—central Africa, southeast Asia, and northeastern Australia—where the effect has been most marked. In northeastern Australia the rain forest is slowly giving way on the margins of the stands to fire and is being replaced by open and more flammable eucalyptus forests. Fire helped to maintain the American prairie on its eastern borders with the deciduous forest. Since the remaining tracts of prairie are small, isolated, and relatively fire-free, trees invade them more easily than in the past.

Fire is an increasingly important factor in a world of people and semiaridity. As an accidental factor its short- and long-term effects can be catastrophic. But as an environmental tool, it can be used quickly and effectively to change or maintain an environment and its vegetation to suit man's needs.

### Gravity

Although ever present, gravity apparently varies little in its biological effects from one part of the earth's surface to another. Without the constant pull of gravity, things would, of course, be chaotic in any earthly ecosystem; roots grow down, stems grow up, and energy is required to move anything against the gravitational pull. The moon and other planets, on the other hand, with their different masses, all have different amounts of gravitational pull and therefore provide gravitational environments much different from that on earth. Hence, the real challenge of gravity (or lack of it) as an environmental factor lies in space.

## Topography

Topography refers to the configuration of the earth's surface: the hills, the valleys, the mountains, the shore; their slope angles and directions, and their elevations. Since the earth's surface is continually being pushed up and eroded down, the relatively flat areas, such as central Illinois, are in the minority. But even in Illinois the microtopography of cornfield furrows produces microenvironmental temperature differences of importance to crop and weed growth.

Topography does not directly affect an organism: it works through other factors. The north- and south-facing slopes of a ravine in Ohio affect plant distribution and growth by their being shaded or sunny, respectively, on an early spring day. The mass of Mount Evans rising 14,258 feet in Colorado lifts the alpine plants on its summit into the winds and bright sun of the thin high altitude atmosphere. Topography provides the setting; it is the other environmental factors that work on the organisms.

## Geologic Substratum

The earth's crust is made up of many sorts of rocks, each with its own particular mineralogical composition and other characteristics. In many places these rocks are the parent materials of the soil and lie as a substratum immediately below the soil. Over large areas, however, the rocks are buried under glacial deposits, alluvium, and dune sands. In such places, the geologic substrata of ecological importance are these unconsolidated deposits that act as the parent materials of the soil.

Soils are the products of climate and vegetation acting upon a geologic substratum. However, within a given climate it is the geologic substratum that causes much of the variation in soils and vegetation. Even in quite different climates, certain kinds of rocks, such as limestone, have pronounced chemical characteristics, which result in the restriction of certain species to these chemically distinct areas. Other species with different requirements may be excluded from the unusual rock. Among the sharpest biological boundaries are those where different rock types come in contact.

The effect of a substratum on soils and vegetation is most marked in dry or cold climates. Here, soil development is slow, so that the particular mineralogical composition of the parent material is often predominant in the thin soil cover. The availability of water in dune sand, salty clays, and rocky soils may be so different that different vegetations occupy them in the same desert climate. Even different kinds of desert animals tend to become restricted to certain substrata because of the nature of their burrow environments or the abundance of food produced by the vegetation on certain substrata as opposed to the scarcity of food on others. The result is a mosaic of ecosystems unmatched in most humid climates, where soil development and subtle vegetational differences tend to mask the effect of the underlying rocks. Nevertheless, even in the humid forests of North Carolina, for example, there are some relatively sharp boundaries between forest types caused by boundaries between rock types. However, these demarcations appear blurred compared to some of the sharp boundaries caused by rock differences in the desert. In the desert, one can literally step from one community to another over the contact zone between two rock types. Rock differences are responsible for the two vegetation types shown in Fig. 2-5.

Whatever the climate, rocks that have an excess or lack of certain minerals tend to cause the greatest biological restriction or exclusion

**Fig. 2-5.** *Sharp vegetational boundary along the contact between two rock types in western Nevada. On the left is an open stand of yellow pines* (Pinus ponderosa *and* P. jeffreyi) *on andesite altered by ancient hot-spring action. On the right is vegetation of pinyon pine* (P. monophylla), *juniper* (Juniperus osteosperma), *sagebrush* (Artemisia), *and grass on andesite which has not been altered.*

of species. These are limestone, serpentine, dolomite, and any rock that has been chemically altered by hot-spring or volcanic action. By contrast, rocks of mixed mineralogic composition, no matter what their origin, tend to have similar vegetations in the same climate. Alluvium, almost always, is the geologic substratum developing into the most productive soils in any climate. Part of this is owing to the variety of minerals present in alluvium and part of it is the result of the unconsolidated but partially weathered nature of the alluvium, which allows relatively rapid development of deep, well-watered soils.

### Soil

It is difficult to separate the effect of soil as an environmental factor from that of the geologic substratum. However, soil is a physical-biological system in itself and is at least as complex as the vegetation above it.

Soils consist of various sizes of mineral material (sand, silt, and clay) derived from the geologic substratum, organic matter from decaying plant and animal materials, water derived from precipitation, air that circulates in the atmosphere above, and fantastic numbers of minute plants and animals.

Each kind of soil has a general structure or organization, and possesses definite physical and biological characteristics. Soils develop over a long period of time and their characteristics reflect the climate during this time, the kind of parent material providing the minerals, and the kind of vegetation supplying the organic matter.

As an environmental factor, soil is extremely complex in its effects. It is the source of mineral nutrients for the whole ecosystem and acts as a reservoir for these nutrients in their cycling through the ecosystem. It is also a great storage reservoir for the water that continuously leaves the soil and moves into and through the plants. Since soil microorganisms and the roots of the higher plants are surrounded by the soil, it is also the source of oxygen for their respiration. The solid portion of most soils remains fairly constant in volume, but the pore space between solid particles may be completely filled with water during and immediately after heavy rains or filled with air during droughts. Most plants grow best when these spaces are not exclusively occupied by either water or air.

Soil has both structure and texture. Structural characteristics are those concerned with the arrangement of soil particles, whereas texture is characterized by the proportions of the different sized particles, such as of sand, silt, and clay.

Most soils also exhibit large morphological characteristics, which one may best discover by digging a pit and viewing the vertical exposure of the soil mass in cross section. This exposure is called a *soil profile*. Most soil profiles consist of layers or "horizons" (see Fig. 2-6). Usually there will be a thin series of organic horizons near the surface corresponding to stages in the decomposition of leaf and twig material. Uppermost will be the fresh leaf litter; under this a layer in which fungi and bacteria have partially broken down the leaves and twigs; and then a layer of humus, which is dark and relatively amorphous organic matter.

The uppermost mineral soil horizon, called the *A* horizon, is a zone that has been considerably leached of certain compounds by percolating rainwater but usually has the greatest root concentration and biological activity. It often has considerable humus mixed with the mineral soil. However, under some kinds of coniferous forests in the north, the *podzol* soils have very little organic matter in the *A* horizon but a considerable depth of raw humus lying above the mineral soil. *Laterite* soils under tropical rain forests have very thin organic horizons and almost no humus in the *A* horizon because of the rapid bacterial and fungal activity at the uniformly high temperature and moisture conditions.

The *B* horizon is the zone of accumulation of minerals and clays and, in podzols, even some organic matter. In most forest soils, the *B* horizon is more dense and sticky and contains fewer roots than the *A* horizon. In grassland and desert soils, the *B* horizon usually exhibits a lime layer, which is the result of weak leaching of calcium from the *A* horizon. The dryer the climate, the closer this lime layer is to the surface.

The *C* horizon is the lower part of the soil; it is in this layer that primary weathering of the parent material takes place. Often it is rocky and may merge imperceptibly with the parent material.

Since the soil is the water and mineral reservoir for the ecosystem, we need to know as much as we can about its structure and textural characteristics, its profile, its ability to hold and release water, its ability to supply minerals, and the biological activity that functions in the recycling of these minerals from dead leaf to humus to ion to root and back to leaf again.

## BIOLOGICAL FACTORS

### Green Plants

The fundamental role of green plants in the ecosystem is the manufacture of food from carbon dioxide and water. All non-green or-

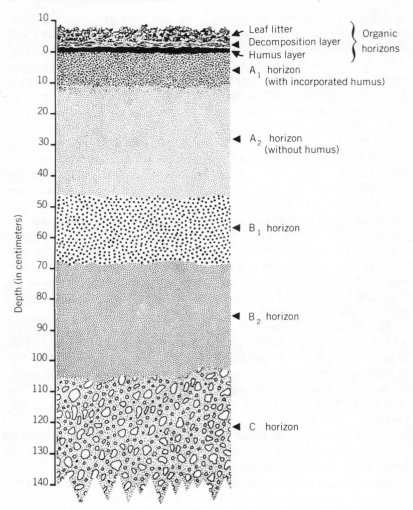

**Fig. 2-6.** *Diagram of the profile of a podzolic soil under an old shortleaf pine* (P. echinata) *stand in North Carolina showing the three organic horizons over the* A, B, *and* C *horizons of the mineral soil.*

ganisms thus need green plants as a part of their direct or indirect environment. All large plants that tend to influence the physical factors of a terrestrial environment also happen to be green plants—trees, shrubs, grasses. They modify almost all environmental factors by shading, using water and minerals from the soil, and adding leaf litter to the soil surface.

Nearby green plants form an important part of the environment of any green plant by competing for light, water, minerals, and space. Such competition (or "interference," Harper, 1961) is almost always indirect—that is, through the depletion of an environmental component such as light or water that is necessary for the success of another individual. Competition can be between individuals of different species or between individuals of about the same size and having the same general environmental requirements. Such competition tends to produce plant diversity in both structure and function in most vegetational types. Often this diversity is morphological and easily detected, but sometimes it is physiological and can be detected only by observation of behavior. Such diversity leads to higher yield of plant material per unit area of land surface because of greater utilization of the environment.

Since root systems are important in competition, a knowledge of their characteristics and volume is necessary. The intensity of root competition is often severe but may not be noticed unless an experimental approach is made. In Fig. 2-7, all the tree roots entering the plots were cut, and competition for water was so reduced that a luxuriant stand of seedling trees appeared on an otherwise almost barren forest floor. Eventually, however, competition among these seedlings for light and water reduced the survivors to only a few.

### Non-green Plants

Non-green plants are of many types; they range from bacteria and fungi to angiosperms such as the Indian pipes of the north and the brilliant red snowplant of the California Sierra. Non-green plants play one of three roles in the ecosystem: (1) decomposers, (2) parasites, or (3) symbionts.

**Decomposers.** These are primarily soil fungi and soil bacteria that break down organic matter into simpler compounds. This process returns elements such as calcium, magnesium, and phosphorus to the soil from which they can be reabsorbed by the higher plants. Some decomposers also fix atmospheric nitrogen in the soil. Without decomposers, of course, organic matter would simply accumulate until the mineral in shortest supply was concentrated in living or dead organic matter and none remained in the root zone of the soil. The production of new protoplasm in the ecosystem by green plants would then stop. In forested regions of the north, organic matter often accumulates to over a foot in depth because low temperature limits the activities of the decomposers. In the tropical rain forests, the process

**Fig. 2-7.** *These pictures show the effects of eliminating root competition in a North Carolina oak-hickory forest. At the time the upper photograph was taken, a trench was dug around the small plot on the forest floor; all tree roots were cut and the trench filled in. The lower photograph was taken three years later and shows the trenched plot filled with many tree seedlings and other plants, while the adjacent untrenched areas are still bare. Photographs by C. F. Korstian.*

34

is just the reverse; organic matter is decomposed rapidly, thus returning nutrients to the soil.

**Parasites.** These are usually pathogenic fungi or bacteria which weaken or kill individual plants and siphon off some of the energy of the ecosystem into their own structures and activity. There are also some angiosperm parasites such as dodder (*Cuscuta*) and bastard toadflax (*Comandra*), the latter a root parasite on sagebrush having green leaves and manufacturing some food. Mistletoes of the family Loranthaceae are also photosynthetically active parasites on woody plants.

Many parasitic fungi are ecologically balanced with their hosts, so that the hosts are not eliminated with consequent elimination of the parasite. This balance probably has been achieved by slow evolution of relatively resistant forms of hosts simultaneously with the evolution of nonvirulent forms of the parasite. What can happen when a virulent parasite is accidentally introduced to a nonresistant species is shown by the case of the chestnut blight in eastern North America. The fungus *Endothia parasitica,* a native of Asia, attacked but did not kill the Chinese chestnut in Asia. The fungus arrived in the United States on some Chinese chestnut seedlings in the 1890s and spread to the native American chestnut, *Castanea dentata,* an important dominant tree in the eastern deciduous forest. This chestnut species had no resistance to *E. parasitica,* even though it served as host to two nonvirulent native Endothias. By the mid-1930s, the American chestnut was dead throughout its range except for some weak stump sprouts, which have shown no signs of real resistance. The chestnut's ecological niche in the eastern forests has been occupied largely by various species of oaks. Thus, even if a resistant strain of chestnut should now be found, it would find the ecological doorway to its old haunts hard to open.

**Symbionts.** These are mainly bacteria and fungi that live in close association with the roots of higher plants. Some benefit accrues to both the non-green plant and its host, often through the role of the bacterium or fungus in making nitrogen available. Examples are the nitrogen-fixing bacteria on the roots of leguminous plants, and the mycorrhizal fungi in the roots of trees and orchids.

## Animals

The major role of animals in a green plant's environment is as a destructive force; animals usually eat or otherwise damage plants. However, the interrelationships between animals and plants in an ecosystem are more complex. Animals are involved in the recycling of minerals, particularly nitrogen. Insects and other animals play an extremely important part in the pollination and thus the reproduction of many of the higher plants. The seeds of many species are normally distributed by or through animals. Animals thus form a necessary part of the environment of most plants.

On the other hand, when animal populations are or become too large for the vegetation to support, destructive change in the vegetation usually occurs. This in turn is often followed by destructive erosion. The destruction of pasture or range vegetation due to over-grazing by domestic stock is well known. In New Zealand, the vegetation evolved in isolation without the presence of grazing mammals. The introduction of domestic sheep and wild deer there seriously damaged much of the native mountain vegetation. Not only has the result been a decrease in productivity of the vegetation, but the weakened vegetation has allowed accelerated erosion of the soil and of the friable graywacke rock. Such range land is literally going downhill.

### Man

Man is the one biological factor that can either make the environment fit his needs or unknowingly ruin it. Because of his increasing population and technological advances, he is changing almost all environments.

Primitive man was essentially a member of the local natural ecosystem. The Plains Indian, before he acquired the horse in the eighteenth century, was a minor part of the great North American prairie ecosystem. The horse made him more effective as a reducer of animal populations, mainly buffalo (bison). But his effect was small compared to that of the invading white man with guns and railroads, who in a few years replaced the old prairie ecosystem by the more efficient cattle-grazing and wheat-farming agriculture.

Whether we like it or not, man must use almost all of the world's arable lands to produce more food if the world's population continues to increase. Scientific agriculture is essentially crop ecology. By knowing the environmental requirements of a crop plant and adjusting the environment to fit these requirements, greater productivity results. Also, new crop plants can be bred to fit new or different environments.

Unfortunately, man has wittingly or unwittingly ignored many ecological and evolutionary principles. Needless destruction of vegetation, erosion, and misuse of land are inexcusable. In his industrial revolution, changing of environments, and modern mobility, man suddenly has made it possible for certain kinds of organisms to become widely dispersed. Some species now have almost worldwide distribution. Many of these adventive species are destructive in the new localities: the English sparrow in America; the rabbit in Australia; the chestnut blight fungus; and the Asiatic plant *Halogeton glomeratus,* which is poisonous to stock in western United States. Until man enabled these organisms to cross oceanic and mountain barriers, they remained in check in their own ecosystems. Now we face a continual battle with invaders of this kind because of our own ecological carelessness.

## ENVIRONMENTAL PRINCIPLES

We know enough now of environmental biology to arrive at some principles that appear to govern organism-environment relationships. Three of these are of considerable importance.

**1. Principle of Limiting Factors.** In the middle of the nineteenth century a German agricultural chemist, Justus von Liebig, found that the yield of a crop could be increased only by supplying the plants more of the nutrient present in least amount. In other words, a field of wheat might have plenty of available phosphorus for a high yield but instead might have a very poor yield because of insufficient nitrogen in the soil. Supplying the crop with more phosphorus would do nothing to improve the situation. However, by adding nitrogen the yield could be increased. Nitrogen is the *limiting factor* in this case, and the crop yield would increase in direct proportion to the amount of nitrogen fertilizer added. Eventually, of course, yield would level off and there would be no increase with addition of nitrogen. At this point, nitrogen is no longer limiting; some other environmental factor becomes limiting, perhaps phosphorus or water. A little experimentation might disclose the controlling factor, thus making it possible to increase the yield again by proper additions.

This increase cannot go on indefinitely, although it is surprising how much increase in yield is possible by removing these minimal factors one by one. Such scientific management has increased corn yields greatly in the American Midwest.

There is an upper limit to these factors also. Too high a temperature is as bad in its way as too low a temperature, too much water as bad as too little water. If too much nitrate fertilizer is added, the results can be disastrous. Therefore, in addition to Liebig's so-called "Law of the Minimum," there is what we might call the "Law of the Maximum." Actually, what should be remembered here is that every organism requires certain amounts of several environmental factors for optimal growth. If there isn't quite enough of a particular factor or a little too much of it, the organism grows poorly. If the amount is too low or far too much, the organism will fail to grow or even die.

Today, instead of speaking of "minimal" factors, we speak of "limiting" factors which limit the growth, reproduction, and, therefore, the distribution of any organism by scarcity or overabundance of that particular factor. Since we are interested in the limitation effects on a single individual or on a given kind of organism, we might say that the principle of limiting factors is an "organism-centered" principle.

**2. Principle of the Holocoenotic Environment.** From the discussion of limiting factors, it is obvious that, as soon as one limiting factor is removed, another takes its place. Also, we know that if one factor in an environment is changed, this change may cause shifts in other environmental components. For example, assume that the temperature of a greenhouse is increased by 10°C. This higher temperature enables the air to hold more water vapor. The temperature increase will also increase the vapor pressure of liquid surfaces within the room. One of the results of this combination of events is an increased evaporation rate. This, of course, will increase the rate of transpiration, which in turn increases absorption of soil moisture. Such reduction of free water in the soil allows air to be drawn into the soil and increases the dryness of the soil. The chain of events branches repeatedly.

This chain illustrates something of the complexity of the environment. In spite of the growth of an organism or community being controlled by limiting factors, we cannot ignore the fact that the environment is really a complex of interacting factors; if one factor is changed, almost all will change eventually. In 1927, Karl Friederich, a German ecologist, pointed out that community-environmental relationships are *holocoenotic*. This means simply that there are no "walls" or barriers between the factors of an environment or between an environment and the organism or biotic community. The ecosystem reacts as a whole; it is practically impossible to wall off a single factor or organism in nature and control it at will without affecting the rest of the ecosystem.

Some of the interactions which are possible even in the environment of a single organism can be seen in Fig. 2-1 (p. 9). It must be remembered also that an ecosystem may be made up of millions of organisms each of which is part of the environment of any other. Thus, any change, no matter how small, is reflected in some way throughout the ecosystem; no "walls" have yet been discovered that prevent these interactions from taking place.

Since this principle primarily concerns interactions in the environment, we may say it is "environment centered."

**3. Principle of Trigger Factors.** When the principle of the holocoenotic environment was first suggested, some ecologists thought that, because of its multifactor approach, it was incompatible with the principle of limiting factors. One of these principles, they said, must not be valid. Is this true? Can a single factor be limiting if the environment acts as a multifactored complex? Can water be limiting in a desert if the water factor is so closely linked to temperature, soil, and other factors? Common sense says "yes" to this latter question.

Let us take the situation in a desert. Here, of course, water is the principal limiting factor. This is easily proved; if one adds a moderate amount of water to the soil around a sagebrush plant, it will grow faster and bigger. If water is added by irrigation to a pasture of desert grasses, the amount of forage will be greatly increased. If good winter rains come to the California deserts, the spring wildflowers will be abundant. What happens when an irrigation ditch overflows into sagebrush land year after year? This does occur occasionally, but to get the answer all one has to do is to observe the willows, cottonwoods, marsh grasses, and rushes that invade the banks of such ditches or grow below them on a hillside where seepage water is available. If water is added continually to desert land, the vegetation will change in a few years into vegetation typical of a river valley. In other words, by completely removing water as a limiting factor, the growth of sagebrush will be temporarily increased. Eventually, however, the environment becomes so favorable for willows and cottonwoods that sagebrush is shaded out—light becomes limiting for sagebrush but larger or more shade-tolerant plants find the new environment quite to their liking.

Thus, the removal of a limiting factor always creates a far-reaching chain reaction in the ecosystem and occasionally the replacement of one ecosystem by another. The factor thus changed becomes a *trigger factor* in starting the chain reaction. Many times, the trigger factor is, indeed, a factor that was limiting but is no longer limiting. On the other hand, a trigger factor may be something not present in the environment before, such as radioactive fallout in the Nevada desert or deer in the New Zealand forests. In either case, whether a limiting factor is changed or a new factor is added, life in that ecosystem is never the same again. Where the changes will lead we often cannot know, although with ecological knowledge we can sometimes make rough guesses.

The trigger-factor principle, unlike the limiting-factor principle, is "environment centered." It is a corollary to and depends upon the holocoenotic principle, which in turn is based on the chain reactions set off by trigger factors themselves. But the fact that many trigger factors are modified limiting factors, shows that all three of these principles are interrelated.

## INTEGRATION OF THE ENVIRONMENT

Since environments act as whole complexes, we must try to measure the impacts of total environments and to classify these environments into recognizable types. There are two approaches one can use in these attempts at integration: one is physical; the other biological. The physical approach follows the movement of energy through the environment by utilizing the energy-budget concept. The biological approach uses the biotic community as an integrating indicator of the whole environmental complex.

**1. Energy Budget as a Measure of Environment.** Since the whole ecosystem is based on energy, the best physical measure of an environment is the amount and disposition of the energy entering and leaving the environmental system. The income, use, and loss of energy in an environment can be expressed by the *energy-budget equation*. Since the discussion here will be brief and simplified, for further information read the discussions by Geiger (1957), Budyko (1958), and Gates (1962). The equation can be stated as follows:

$$S + R + LE + G + C = 0$$

where

$S =$ solar radiation

$R =$ infrared thermal radiation from earth and atmosphere

$L =$ latent heat of evaporation and condensation

$E =$ amount of evaporation and condensation

$G =$ sensible heat by conduction in the soil

$C =$ flow of heat by conduction and convection from the soil to the atmosphere and vice versa

The above components are considered to be positive when energy is flowing into a layer at the ground surface, and negative when flowing away from this surface.

The ultimate source of energy in an environment is solar radiation consisting mostly of visible wavelengths. At the outer edge of the atmosphere, it arrives from the sun at a rate of about 2 calories per sq cm per minute. However, as it passes through the atmosphere, it is depleted by reflection from clouds and dust, and absorption by atmospheric gases. By the time solar radiation arrives at the vegetation surface, its rate may be down to 1 calorie per sq cm per minute, more or less, depending on the amount of cloudiness and density of the atmosphere. Some of this remainder is reflected by the soil and vegetation and is thus lost into space. Some is absorbed by the soil and raises the soil temperature. Some, also, is absorbed by the vegetation, but plant temperatures usually are not increased much because this heat is used in the transpiration of water and also is conducted rapidly into the air around the leaf.

The solar energy absorbed by atmospheric gases and cloud droplets is radiated as infrared, some out into space and some downward to earth as sky thermal radiation. The solar energy absorbed by the earth is radiated upward as infrared; this can be called "terrestrial thermal radiation" ($R$). This thermal radiation goes on continuously, but, of course, at varying rates, while solar radiation ($S$) comes in only during the day and is considerably reduced during the winter. Normally, thermal radiation is negative at the earth's surface, whereas solar radiation is positive during the day and zero at night. The sum of solar radiation plus thermal radiation plus reflection is called *net radiation*. Net radiation, in other words, is the result of incoming solar radiation and outgoing reflected radiation, and incoming and outgoing thermal radiation. Net radiation is normally positive during the daytime because of the excess of solar radiation over thermal-radiation losses. Conversely, net radiation is usually negative at night because of the lack of solar radiation and the continuance of thermal radiation.

It is the energy of net radiation that is available for evaporation of water, movement of heat into soil or water, and the heating of the lower air. Thus, the greater the net radiation, the more evaporation there is, the more heating of the soil and water bodies, and the more heating of the lower air. In winter in the northern United States, net radiation may be negative, so that instead of evaporation there is condensation (as ice crystals or frost), the soil and water lose heat (and the lakes freeze), and the lower air loses heat to the snow-covered soil and ice. On the other hand, net radiation figures are high for tropical oceans—evaporation is high, the water is warm, and the air is balmy.

The annual curve of net radiation is a good indication of environment. However, in order to evaluate how the net radiation is used in an environment, the annual curves for other components of the energy budget must also be known, particularly $LE$, which is concerned with rate and amount of evaporation and condensation, and $C$, the heat flow between the soil or water and the lower air.

Figure 2-8 shows how some environments differ in net radiation and how it is used up during the year. Notice the uniformity in net radiation throughout the year at Manáos, Brazil, in the Amazonian rain forest, and how it is used mostly in evaporation of the always available water. However, there is always enough heat left over to keep the air warm. Compare that tropical cloudy environment with the one at Turukhansk, Siberia, where net radiation is positive only during the summertime and, therefore, available for evaporation and heating of the air and soil only during those summer months. At sunny Aswan, Egypt, there is little or no water to evaporate and the net-radiation energy is used almost entirely to heat the air; the result is a hot desert.

Environments, then, can be characterized physically by measuring incoming and outgoing energy. Instruments and techniques for doing this are now used by ecologists, meteorologists, climatologists, and geographers. The energy-budget approach is perhaps the best quantitative method now available for measuring the total impact of the physical part of the environment.

**2. Vegetation as a Measure of Total Environment.** To the experienced ecologist, vegetation can be a very sensitive indicator of conditions in the *total* environment. Although the energy-budget approach, using instruments, is fundamental for measuring the nature of the physical environment, the structure and rate of change in vegetational composition provide an indication of the nature of the *whole* environment, biological as well as physical.

The assembling of individuals of various plant species into a plant community is the result of the total environment working through time on the available flora. As a result, vegetation is a delicate integrator of environmental conditions and can be used as an indicator of such conditions.

Although there is no instrument that can do as well, vegetation has a few disadvantages as an environmental indicator:

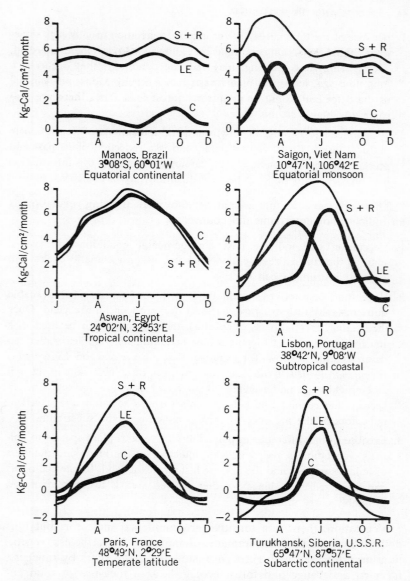

**Fig. 2-8.** *Annual cycles of energy-budget components at six different locations on the earth's surface in kilogram-calories per square centimeter per month.* S + R *is the net radiation at the surface,* C *is the heat transferred to or from the surface by convection or turbulence, and* LE *is the heat transferred by evaporation or condensation. Diagrams from Gates (1962), using data of Budyko (1958).*

1. Because of the time necessary for growth, vegetation usually lags somewhat behind the actual conditions that allowed it to become established. Trees, being slow growing, may indicate conditions that occurred a long time ago; lodgepole pine forests in the Rocky Mountains can tell us the dates and extent of prehistoric forest fires. Thus there are also some advantages to this lag.

2. It is difficult to express the environmental indications of vegetation in physical terms. Every vegetational stand is a reflection of its past and present total environment, but we cannot yet transpose this information into physical units that can be used quantitatively in equations.

There are some definite advantages, however, in using vegetation as an indicator of environmental conditions:

1. Vegetation can indicate past environmental conditions or events, such as the forest fires mentioned above, or past climatic cycles. No physical instrument can do this.

2. Vegetation can tell us much about soil conditions: salts, available nutrients, physical structure, capacity for crop or timber yield. Once the original correlation is established, the vegetation can be used as a soil indicator without digging a hole or taking soil samples. American desert ecologists know, for example, that big greasewood (*Sarcobatus vermiculatus*) usually indicates the presence of soluble salts in the soil and brackish ground water 1 to 30 feet below the surface. Certain species that require unusual elements such as selenium are excellent indicators of the presence of certain minerals in the substratum.

3. Because of the difference in palatability of various plant species to animals, vegetation is a very delicate indicator of the kinds and numbers of animals present and the grazing history of the land. Range ecologists can often tell at a glance whether a given area is overgrazed or can profitably carry more stock.

Vegetation, then, is a sensitive environmental indicator, but it is difficult to make the measurements quantitative. Nevertheless, vegetation has been used with excellent results for many years by ranchers, farmers, and range and forest ecologists as a measure of total environmental conditions and the trend of these conditions. Although it takes training and knowledge to "read" vegetation, no instrument has yet been devised, or probably ever will be, that is as sensitive as vegetation.

# 3

# THE INDIVIDUAL
# PLANT AND
# ITS ENVIRONMENT

The distribution of a species and the productivity of an ecosystem both depend upon the success or failure of individual plants. Therefore, it is necessary that we know how different kinds of individuals operate under the impact of different kinds of environments. Also we need to know the relative effects of varying certain environmental components. Success or failure of a plant depends largely upon relative rates of processes within the plant as these processes are affected by the environment. This field of investigation is the province of *physiological ecology*—the study of organic processes in an individual under natural environmental conditions or in controlled environments. Physiological ecology is a borderline science between physiology and ecology and may be approached from either discipline.

The data of physiological ecology can be obtained in two ways: (1) in the field under natural conditions, or (2) in the controlled environments of the laboratory or growth chamber. Both approaches have advantages. The field method provides natural amounts of environmental components such as light and certain soil characteristics, and thus is more typical of the conditions the plant normally experiences. But there are certain techniques that are relatively difficult to work with under field conditions. Also, it is almost impossible to control the field environment so that the effects of contrasting amounts of a given component can be studied. With the development of modern lighting and thermostatically controlled heating and cooling systems, it has been possible to build large, controlled environment facilities (such as the Earhart Laboratory at the California Institute of Technology). Also commercially available, and considerably cheaper and more adaptable to most problems, are many kinds of small, controlled environment chambers. In a chamber of any size, the big problem is to get consistent lighting of solar intensity over a large enough space so that more than just a few plants can be grown without creating too much of a heat load. Natural sunlight, while easy and cheap to use, is notoriously variable because of clouds and time of year. Thus, neither field measurements nor laboratory measurements provide all the answers. Most problems in physiological ecology require both approaches.

A number of years ago, British ecologists started compiling a series of reports on ecological life histories of common wild plants in Britain. Today this series is of great value as a source of information on plant growth requirements and tolerances. Abundant information of this type is available for crop plants; the physiological ecology of tomato or corn, for example, is well known compared to that of most wild plants. Aside from the purely scientific importance of such knowledge, there is great practical value in knowing how the life cycle of a weed, a forest tree, or a meadow grass is affected by the environment.

It will be remembered that the environment of a plant is continually changing both cyclically and cumulatively from the time it germinates until its death. Temperature, photoperiod, and soil mois-

**Fig. 3-1.** Oxyria digyna, *alpine sorrel, in its natural alpine habitat of rock crevices above timberline in the Medicine Bow Mountains, Wyoming.*

ture conditions are quite different, of course, during the autumn, when the seed of winter wheat is planted and germinates, from the conditions prevailing early the following summer, when the wheat plant matures, produces new seed, and dies.

An example of a wild plant species whose ecology we know something about (Mooney and Billings, 1961) is the alpine sorrel, *Oxyria digyna* (Fig. 3-1). It is a relative of the common weedy dock, and also of the buckwheat. Alpine sorrel is widely distributed in the Arctic and in the high-mountain regions of North America and Eurasia, growing primarily where snow does not melt until midsummer. Its type of distribution is termed "circumboreal," meaning that it occurs around the earth in northern latitudes.

As an example of the life history approach to ecology, we will consider important events during the life of an alpine sorrel plant as it grows on a scree slope at an elevation of about 9,100 feet on Elephant's Back, a mountain near Carson Pass in the California Sierra Nevada. For convenience we can divide the life cycle into three main parts: *germination; vegetative growth;* and *flowering and fruiting.*

### Germination

The small winged seeds of *Oxyria* at Carson Pass ripen in August or September. They have the ability to germinate immediately after they fall from the parent plant into the crevices in the rocks where there is a bit of soil and some light. In the Sierra, however, August and September conditions are usually too dry for germination. The snow around the plants has long since melted, and the water has seeped too deeply into the rock crevices to benefit the seeds. Also, rain is rare in the Sierra at this time of year. Temperatures are usually adequate for germination in early September, but without water it will not occur. Lack of water appears to be the principal limiting factor in preventing germination of the seed during the year in which it is produced.

The snows come in early autumn and the temperature drops while the seed lies in the cold, dark pocket of soil in the crevice. During this winter period many things may be limiting: water is frozen and nonavailable; the temperature is far too low for germination; and the deep snowpack above (often 15 to 30 feet deep in the high Sierra) cuts out the necessary light.

It is late June, July, or even August before the snowbank on the scree melts away. The melting snow provides water for germination, light now penetrates the rock crevices, and the temperature rises. A few seeds may germinate by the time the mean soil temperature has risen to 10°C (50°F), but most of them will not germinate until the mean temperature rises above 15°C (about 59°F). Since the temperature drops to freezing or below almost every night, it may take several days for germination to occur because sufficient heat is available only during part of the day. It is a race to get enough heat to develop a primary root system before the soil in the crevice dries out. Usually only a few seedlings are successful; seedling establishment is difficult and rare in alpine environments. Growth is often slowed by low temperatures to such an extent that the available water in the crevice evaporates before the seedling becomes established. Alpine sorrel, like most alpine and arctic plants, benefits by being a perennial plant; an annual species would have to go through this difficult seedling establishment almost every year to maintain the population. Once a perennial plant like *Oxyria* is established, the individual may live and produce seeds for many years. This characteristic is a decided advantage where low temperatures allow such a short season for seedling establishment.

**Vegetative Growth**

After germination, growth of alpine sorrel is rather slow. Some seedlings become successfully established and carry on enough photosynthesis to provide stored food for winter respiration and for the sudden start of growth in the following year after the snow melts. Other seedlings, for one reason or another, may fail to develop enough root system to provide water through the late summer drought, and thus they die. Some summers may be too dry for any seedlings to survive.

Assume that the seedling becomes established before late summer. It does not flower this first summer because it is making and storing just enough food to get it through the winter and the initial burst of growth at the start of the next summer. As the days become shorter, the decrease in day length causes a dormant bud to be formed. The snows return again in early autumn, the leaves die, but the roots and the perennating bud remain alive deep under the snow. The deep snow insulates the bud and roots from severe cold and from excessive water loss; either event will kill the seedling.

During the winter, the plant is respiring, but at such a slow rate, because of the low temperature, that relatively little of the food stored in the roots is used up. It remains under the snow nine months or more. The midsummer melting of the snow exposes the rocks and the bud to the bright sun and blue Sierran sky. During the daytime, the rocky environment warms up. This increase in temperature causes an increase in respiration rate, water absorption, and digestion of root starch, and the plant is ready to grow. But one more thing is neces- sary before the bud breaks dormancy and sends up an aerial shoot; by chemical means, it measures the length of the photoperiod and, if it exceeds a certain minimum number of hours, bud dormancy is broken and the aerial shoot begins to grow. If, however, through some freak of weather the snow over the sorrel plant melted by early spring and the rocks and soil warmed up, the plant would still remain dormant, and in all likelihood cold weather would return again and the plant would be covered again with snow. This photo- periodic sensitivity required for breaking of dormancy is insurance against premature emergence into the changeable weather of April and May. It also works in reverse. When September comes with its shorter days, the upper part of the plant begins to die back and a new perennating bud forms. Even though most days of September and October are warm enough for growth, this is the season when a few days of bitter weather following an early snowstorm could cause serious damage to a nondormant plant. *Oxyria* grows under low summer temperature conditions, but it can be killed by a sudden drop in temperature when it is in the nondormant state.

These photoperiodic requirements for alpine sorrel were found by a group from Duke University who began by collecting seeds from *Oxyria* plants at Carson Pass and other arctic and alpine locations in North America. These seeds were planted in controlled environmental chambers in the laboratory. Here, the plants were grown on typical mountain and arctic summer temperature cycles. The young plants then were divided into three groups. One group was given a daily photoperiod of 12 hours; another group was given 15 hours of light a day; the third group was given continuous light. The plants with 12 hours of light formed perennating buds and remained dormant. Within eight weeks all of the Sierran alpine sorrels receiving 15 hours of light had grown vegetatively, flowered, and produced seeds. The plants receiving continuous light also all broke dormancy and produced flowers and seeds, but it took several weeks longer for this to occur than it did under the 15-hour treatment. The latitude of Carson Pass is just under 39 degrees North; this makes the maximum photoperiod there, which occurs in late June, just about 15 hours. Through evolution the Carson Pass alpine sorrels have developed a built-in photoperiod timer that will not let them break dormancy under the 12-hour photoperiod of spring no matter how warm and balmy the air is. But when the longer days of summer come, dormancy is broken.

Even though the Sierran days are never longer than 15 hours, the Sierran sorrels theoretically could be grown even in the Arctic with its long days. But growth evidently would not be as rapid as in the Sierra, and the transplanted Sierran plants probably would not be very successful. However, if the Carson Pass sorrels were transplanted to the high Andes in Ecuador on the equator, where the days are always 12 hours long, the plants would probably fail to grow no matter how favorable the temperature and moisture conditions.

The great burst of growth in *Oxyria* comes soon after the breaking of dormancy. This growth is largely at the expense of food stored in the roots; digestion rates and respiration rates are high. During this growth many new leaves are formed, and they quickly turn green and begin to carry on photosynthesis. Some of this new food is stored in the roots as sugar and starch and some is used to help produce the flowering stalk and seeds.

Photosynthesis rates can be measured by determining the amount of $CO_2$ used in a given amount of time by the plant from an airstream of known $CO_2$ concentration. Conversely, respiration rates can be determined by putting a plant in the dark and measuring its output of $CO_2$ in a certain time period. Since a plant in the light simultaneously carries on both photosynthesis and respiration, it both uses and releases $CO_2$. The net $CO_2$ exchange between plant and air is equivalent to *net photosynthesis,* the amount of carbon "fixed" or made into food in excess of the immediate respiratory needs of the leaves. Net photosynthesis is what is actually measured in $CO_2$ exchange measurements. To determine *total* or *gross photosynthesis,* the amount of $CO_2$ released in respiration must be added to the net photosynthesis rate.

The photosynthetic rate depends on many environmental variables; two of the most important are light and temperature. At 20°C (68°F) in bright light, net photosynthesis rates in alpine sorrel plants, such as those at Carson Pass, are about 4 milligrams of $CO_2$ made into food for every gram of fresh leaves per hour. The respiration rate of such leaves at 20°C is about 1 milligram of $CO_2$ released for every gram of fresh leaves per hour. Gross photosynthesis of *Oxyria* under these conditions, therefore, would be about 5 milligrams of $CO_2$ converted into food for every gram of fresh leaves per hour. The leaves use about 20 per cent of this gross amount in respiration. Most of the remaining 80 per cent is translocated to the roots where a small amount is respired and the greater part stored as carbohydrate.

Not many data are yet available on the carbon metabolism of *whole* alpine sorrel plants in relation to various combinations of light and temperature. But we (Scott and Billings, 1964) do have some data of this type obtained experimentally on plants of *Poa alpina,* the alpine bluegrass, an associate of alpine sorrel throughout much of its range. The bluegrass plants used were grown from seed obtained at 11,000 feet in the Medicine Bow Mountains of Wyoming. Measurements were made of the carbon metabolism of *whole* plants at many combinations of light and temperature. The graph in Fig. 3-2 shows the results. Optimal conditions for gain occur between 9,000 and 10,000 foot-candles (almost full sunlight) at temperatures between 10° and 20°C. The mean light and temperature conditions hour by hour for a cloudy, cold day at that altitude and a bright, sunny day are plotted over the metabolism graph. On the sunny day, an alpine bluegrass plant in the Medicine Bow Mountains theoretically would have gained 49 mg $CO_2$ per gm dry weight per 24 hours, but even on the cloudy, cold, snowy day it would have gained 28 mg $CO_2$ per gm. This gain could not have been accomplished by less hardy plants. If we had data of this type for alpine sorrel, the rates would probably be comparable, although the Sierran form might not do so well on a cloudy, cold day.

Before flowering, then, the alpine sorrel has to grow rapidly, produce a number of leaves, and make enough food to help take care of growth during the present year and part of next. It has to do all of this relatively quickly and during the short periods each day when temperature and light are suitable. At the same time, of course, other processes are also going on fairly rapidly. *Oxyria* is almost an obligate snowbank species in the Sierra. Partly this is because it apparently has no "built-in" control of transpiration. Its stomates stay open all day, thus facilitating carbon dioxide fixation, but its transpiration rate continues to climb with increase in evaporation stress. It shows no depression of transpiration rate under high atmospheric aridity as do some of its neighbors on dry, less snowy, ridges. On a warm, bright Sierran afternoon an *Oxyria* plant will lose about 3 gm water per $dm^2$ leaf surface per hour while it is converting only 5 mg of carbon dioxide into food. Apparently, sufficient water is available to the roots to maintain this rate for several hours in the afternoon.

### Flowering and Fruiting

Once the Sierran alpine sorrel plant accumulates enough stored food in its roots to produce leaves and a flowering stalk, it is ripe to flower. But, of course, it will not flower unless the snow melts away early enough to expose the plant to photoperiods of 14–15 hours. An arctic *Oxyria* grown at Carson Pass will not flower, but most

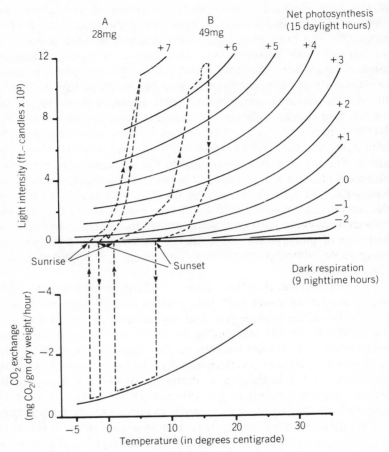

**Fig. 3-2.** *Net photosynthesis of whole plants of alpine bluegrass at different temperatures and light intensities. A plus sign indicates that the whole plant was gaining in carbon compounds at any combination of light and temperature along that particular curve; a minus sign indicates net loss of carbon compounds because respiration exceeded photosynthesis. A= metabolic activity and net gain of $CO_2$ per gram dry weight of tissue during 24 hours of cold, cloudy weather. B= same, for 24 hours of warmer, clear weather. Data of Scott and Billings (1964).*

native Carson Pass *Oxyrias* will bloom every year after they once get started, unless the snow lies very late. Even then, some individuals in the population, because of certain inherited characteristics, are able to bloom after being exposed to day lengths as short as 13 hours.

This variation in the population away from the average requirement of 14 to 15 hours allows seeds to be produced by some individuals even in a year in which the snow stays almost through August. It gives the total population more environmental versatility than any single individual.

Once the Sierran *Oxyria* has flowered, seed are produced rather quickly. The plant is apparently wind-pollinated and may be self-pollinated since it is not self-sterile. This latter characteristic is also an advantage since alpine *Oxyrias* often grow isolated from each other on the scree slopes and insects are not particularly attracted to the plant.

In the Arctic, *Oxyrias* form rhizomes (which they do not in the Sierra) and grow close together because of vegetative reproduction by the rhizomes. Sierran *Oxyria* plants, however, are dependent upon the production of fertile seed whether produced by self-pollination or wind-pollination. At any rate, abundant fertile seed are produced and, in the late summer mountain breeze, blow into crevices of the rocky slopes, completing the life cycle.

# 4

# THE GEOGRAPHIC
# DISTRIBUTION
# OF PLANTS

The existence of any organism anywhere is subject to the "approval" of the local environment. Ecologists are very much interested, therefore, in *where* different kinds of plants grow as well as *why* they grow there.

Any plant species is discontinuously distributed. That is, there are gaps between individuals and clumps that are occupied by individuals of other species. Sometimes these gaps are only a few inches across; in many cases, they are miles across or even hundreds of miles. It is easy to see that any one species has two levels of distribution. The greater of these, which may be called "macrodistribution" or "geographic distribution," can be plotted on a map by dots or generalized distribution boundary lines, as in Fig. 4-1. Within these large areas, the species occurs only here and there in certain kinds of environmental situations such as, perhaps, north-facing limestone cliffs or edges of mountain brooks. This level of distribution may be termed "microdistribution" or "ecological distribution."

There are on the earth today at least 225,000 species of flowering plants, more than 9,000 species of ferns, and only about 700 species of gymnosperms. These all make up the earth's vascular plant flora. Most of these species have no tolerance for cold weather and are confined to the tropics or subtropics. For example, Brazil, which is largely tropical, has a native flora of at least 40,000 species of vascular plants; the subtropical southeastern United States has about 5,000 species; the temperate northern United States and southern Canada have about 4,400 species; whereas the entire Canadian Arctic Archipelago has only 340 species.

The same kind of decrease in numbers of species can be seen altitudinally in Colorado from the relatively warm lowlands to the cold

**Fig. 4-1.** *The general distribution of* Oxyria digyna, *alpine sorrel, in North America. This species shows a typical arctic-alpine distribution pattern and is also found in the arctic and alpine regions of Eurasia. From Mooney and Billings (1961).*

alpine tundra of the Rocky Mountains. Cold tolerance is evidently a scarce commodity in the evolution of the tropical-centered vascular plants. Semiarid regions are somewhat more favored with species; Arizona, for example, has about 3,400 species, which is fairly high considering its relatively small area. California has about 4,000 species, mainly because of its topographic and climatic diversity. Both in Arizona and California the desert floras are relatively rich. Apparently, evolution in the direction of drought resistance is somewhat easier and has more solutions than evolution toward low temperature tolerance. However, the really extreme deserts such as the Atacama in northern Chile, where soil moisture is almost nonexistent for years at a time, provide an almost insurmountable challenge.

## GEOGRAPHIC DISTRIBUTION OF SPECIES

A few species of vascular plants, especially certain grasses, are widely distributed geographically over the earth. While some of these are cosmopolitan—that is, found almost everywhere, there really are no truly cosmopolitan species. However, there are several cosmopolitan genera, of which the best example is *Senecio*. The presence or absence of a winter separates widely distributed species into three groups: the *arctic-alpine* and the *temperate* group, both of which experience winters; and the *pantropical* group, which does not.

Opposed to these wide-ranging species are those with restricted distributions, found only in one area. These are called *endemic species*. There are several levels of endemism, but we will consider only two here: the broad endemics, which are restricted to a given geographic floristic region such as eastern North America or western Europe; and the narrow endemics, which are restricted to certain microenvironments in a narrow geographic range.

Between the wide-ranging species and the endemics are the discontinuous species whose ranges occur in two or more parts often separated by thousands of miles of ocean or great land masses. We will consider in detail only six distribution types: (1) arctic-alpine, (2) temperate, (3) pantropical, (4) broad endemic, (5) narrow endemic, and (6) discontinuous.

### Arctic-Alpine

Probably no more than 100 species make up this group. They are almost entirely perennial herbs. Some are grasses and sedges; some are dicotyledons. All of them occur almost circumboreally around the periphery of the Arctic Ocean as tundra plants; in addition, they are found far to the south in high mountains, notably the Rocky Mountains, the Alps, the Caucasus, and the Himalayas. Some arctic-alpine plants, such as the grasses *Trisetum spicatum* and *Deschampsia caespitosa,* occur sporadically throughout the Andes down into the Southern Hemisphere. They also occur in the mountains of New Zealand and Australia. In their geographic spread, as great as that of any vascular plant, they come close to being geographically cosmopolitan; but ecologically they are not cosmopolitan because they are restricted to cold, snowy places. It is remarkable, though, that they occur in almost all the available environments of this type, no matter how far apart.

## Temperate

Species in this group are distributed widely throughout the moister parts of the northern temperate zone, and a few also range to the Southern Hemisphere. Many of these temperate, widespread species are weeds that have the genetic capacity to produce individuals adapted to different climatic types and have well-adapted dispersal techniques to get there. Dandelion (*Taraxacum vulgare*) and English plantain (*Plantago lanceolata*) are good examples of such cosmopolitan temperate weeds.

## Pantropical

Plants of this type are almost universal throughout the tropics, particularly in areas of cultivation or occupancy by man since many of them are weeds. Pantropical species are rare in the undisturbed rain forest; but in the grasslands, along roadsides and sandy shores, and in the gardens, lawns, and pastures, they are fairly common. Such disturbed and open environments are so similar microclimatically all through the tropics that it is not surprising to see these same kinds of plants growing in such widely separated places. Some of them indeed may have been distributed by floating or being carried across the seas by natural means. However, man in his comings and goings of the last thousand years has purposely or accidentally carried seeds of many of these species to new places. Long ago, the Polynesians moving eastward across the Pacific to Samoa and Tahiti carried yams, candlenuts, and other valuable plants with them from the Indo-Malaysian flora of the southwestern Pacific. Centuries later, they carried these and others northward to unsettled Hawaii, where today they are common members of the wild flora of the islands.

The most widely distributed tree of the tropics is the coconut palm, *Cocos nucifera*. It is found in fringing groves wherever there are sandy shores and enough rain. Much of its wide distribution may be due to the relative tolerance of the large seed to salt water and to the winds and currents that carry the nuts from one shore to another. Also, since this tree is valuable for food and thatch, much of its wide distribution may be due to man.

Many pantropical weeds are members of the Euphorbiaceae or Leguminosae; many are grasses. A good example is *Cynodon dactylon*, a grass that spreads rapidly by both rhizomes and seeds. It is present almost everywhere in the tropics either as a weed or as a needed lawn grass or forage plant. With so wide a range, no wonder that what a Floridian calls "Bermuda grass," a Hawaiian calls "mananea," and a South African calls "kweek" are actually all the same species.

## Broad Endemic

Most vascular species belong to this group—that is, they are restricted to a single floristic region. A floristic region is an area, large or small, that has a relatively distinct flora at the species level. Naturally, there are seldom sharp boundaries between floristic regions, and it is a matter of expert opinion where the boundaries should be drawn. Professor Ronald Good of England (1953) has divided the earth into 37 floristic regions. These range in size from the very large Euro-Siberian region down to such small island regions as Hawaii and Juan Fernandez in the Pacific Ocean. But each is characterized by a flora rather distinct from that of any other region. This flora to a great extent is characterized by the broadly endemic genera and species that are confined to it. Most of the species in the forests, deserts, or mountains of one's own region are broad endemics. In the eastern United States, good examples are flowering dogwood (*Cornus florida*), white oak (*Quercus alba*), sugar maple (*Acer saccharum*), and tulip tree (*Liriodendron tulipifera*). In the West, California poppy (*Eschscholzia californica*), sagebrush (*Artemisia tridentata*), and ponderosa pine (*Pinus ponderosa*) are all typical examples of broad endemics.

## Narrow Endemic

Some species are restricted in their native range to very small areas of a few acres or a few square miles and have such narrow ranges of tolerance for environmental conditions that there is almost no other part of the world in which they could live. Most endemics of this type are restricted by the rare occurrence of a certain type of rock in a restricted type of climate. California, because it has the only Mediterranean type of climate on the North American continent and because it has many kinds of rocks, has a fair share of narrow endemics. Plants of the serpentine outcrops in the inner Coast Ranges of Lake County, north of San Francisco, are good examples.

On the other hand, some narrow endemics could do very well elsewhere—they just haven't had the time or opportunity to travel. They may be young species still more or less restricted to the neighborhood of their origin. Or they may be old species, once widely distributed, which have been caught genetically unprepared in a changing world and have found refuge in a little remainder of their former environment. Tucked away in the Southern Appalachians are relict endemics of this type such as *Shortia galacifolia*. Sandwiched between the coastal California mountains and the foggy sea are others such as the redwood, *Sequoia sempervirens*. Both of these are now planted as ornamentals in many of the cool damp parts of the world but, until man brought them out of their hiding places, they were backed into corners by the advancing warmth and aridity of modern climates.

## Discontinuous

In a sense, almost all plant species are discontinuously distributed. But here we are concerned only with those in which the discontinuities are of the order of several hundred or several thousands of miles. The nineteenth-century American botanist Asa Gray first called attention to the many "species" that occur in both eastern North America and eastern Asia but are missing from western Europe. Today we recognize many of these "species" as consisting of one or more species confined to each of the two areas but extremely closely related within their genera. Such species have been separated from each other long enough to have evolved slightly different structural and physiological characteristics, but they have not been separated long enough to be very different. In fact, even now some of these discontinuous plants appear to belong to a single species.

What could have caused such a distinctive set of distributions? Much of the answer lies in Pleistocene continental glaciation. Four times in the last million years glaciers swept down across Europe. The result was total or selective destruction of the magnificent European Tertiary forests. The glaciers, however, stopped short in southeastern North America and southeastern Asia, both of which extend farther south than Europe, and left ice-free refuges such as the Southern Appalachian Mountains and the mountains of Japan, and Szechwan and Kwangsi in China. In these refuges, many forest species survived the rigorous environments and ice of the Pleistocene but were isolated from their relatives. As the ice began its last retreat about 11,000 years ago, a migration began out of the refuges, particularly in North America, which has resulted in some of the species having relatively broad distributions on at least one of the continents.

But other species, particularly in Asia and to some extent in the Southern Appalachians, have not moved from their protected refuges. Either they lack the ability to disperse seeds easily, or the climate outside their area is not suitable, or both. Time has been long enough in many cases to allow the development of two distinct species from the common Tertiary ancestor: one species in North America, one in Asia. Many of the ancestral species also occurred in Europe before the ice, as is shown by fossils; but the ice moved down over the European forests and destroyed them. The bitter climate prevailing between the ice and the Mediterranean Sea eliminated others. Some examples of these eastern Asiatic–eastern American discontinuous genera are *Liriodendron* (tulip tree), *Liquidambar* (sweet gum), *Menispermum* (moonseed), and *Hamamelis* (witch hazel).

There are also some pronounced discontinuities in species distributions between the Northern and Southern Hemispheres, which are separated by the barrier of the tropics. These are not so easily explained as the Asiatic-American discontinuity. The most extreme cases are those of Northern Hemisphere arctic-alpine species. For example, *Trisetum spicatum,* a common arctic-alpine grass, is also found in the Southern Andes of South America and in the mountains of New Zealand and Australia. As in the Asiatic-American situation, several of these discontinuous species have continued to evolve in isolation so that they now are somewhat different genetically. Several arctic-alpine lichen species have the same distribution pattern.

Just as puzzling are several Californian species found in Chile. The common creosote bush (*Larrea divaricata*) of our southwestern deserts is also common in western Argentina. These north-south discontinuities in species of semiarid environments provide a real challenge in plant geographic research.

## EXPLANATIONS FOR PRESENT DISTRIBUTIONS

After the distribution of a species has been determined, we must ask why it grows there and not somewhere else. We can answer this question in theory fairly well, but the specifics for most plant species are lacking.

### Tolerance Ranges and Present Distributions

If a plant is growing and reproducing in a certain location, there is no better indication that the particular environment lies within the tolerance range of that plant. The tolerance range of an individual plant is that range of environmental conditions in which the plant will grow. Environmental conditions just within the tolerance range will produce only weak, vegetative plants. The plant will flower and produce viable seed only if conditions are well within the tolerance range.

Tolerance ranges are based on physiological requirements; since the kinds and rates of physiological processes are determined by the kinds of genes present, it follows that tolerance ranges are genetically determined. Every individual has its own genotype and its own tolerance range. The more genetic variety there is in a population or a species, the greater the tolerance range of that population or species is likely to be. A vegetatively reproducing population, because of the genetic similarity of its individuals, usually has a narrower tolerance range than a sexually reproducing population of the same species.

A possible example is the aspen tree (*Populus tremuloides*) in the Rocky Mountains, which reproduces vegetatively by root suckers so that a single aspen grove is fairly uniform genetically. In the Great Lakes region this same species also reproduces by seeds and thus a population is genetically mixed and should (as a population) exhibit greater tolerance to a wider range of environmental conditions. However, it is difficult to say whether the Great Lakes aspens are in fact more tolerant of a wide range of environmental conditions than those in the Rocky Mountains. Theoretically at least, we can say this: the tolerance range of a population is equal to the sum of the tolerance ranges of its individuals; the tolerance range of a species is equal to the sum of the tolerance ranges of its local populations. In other words, a species has a much greater tolerance range than that of any of its members.

Here, we might clarify the distinctions between tolerance range, ecologic range, geographic range, and potential geographic range. *Tolerance range* is that range of environmental conditions in which plants of a given species will grow if its seeds, spores, or other propagules can get there. *Ecologic range* is that range of environmental conditions in which the plants of the species actually do grow. *Geographic range* is the geographic limit of the ecologic range. *Potential geographic* range is the geographic limit of possible environments open to the species as determined by its tolerance range and assuming that it can get there by some means or other.

Because plants continue to evolve to some degree, their tolerance ranges are gradually changing. At the same time, earthly environments are also changing to a greater or lesser extent. As a result, ecologic ranges change. As the ecologic range of a species changes, the probability is great that its geographic range will change.

Most species are migrating now, and have migrated in the past. Probably no species, except perhaps some very narrow endemics, has completely occupied its potential geographic range. There are several reasons for this: barriers in the form of oceans, mountain ranges, deserts, or even great forests; low mobility of the seeds or other reproductive structures; or other plants with similar tolerance ranges already occupying its ecological niche in the ecosystem. Given enough time, all of these eventually may be overcome.

Unknowingly man has considerably cut down this time factor

by giving free transportation to many geographically restricted species which either had broad tolerance ranges or were geographically isolated from great areas of their potential geographic range. The result in the last century has been a great explosive migration around the world not only of weedy vascular plants but of fungi, bacteria, insects, birds, and even mammals. Distribution patterns of many organisms are changing as never before. With transportation available and frequent to even isolated areas, these migrations and invasions by broadly tolerant species represent a serious threat to the existence of native but narrowly tolerant species in all parts of the world. Man must control these uncontrolled migrations, for they seldom are beneficial.

## Structure of Species and Present Distributions

In order to understand why some species have broad tolerance ranges and some have narrow tolerance ranges, we must understand the structure of species. The basic building block of the species is the individual organism. The individual is a working physiological system whose ability to operate in a given range of environments is determined by its genes and by the conditioning of the environment itself. Thus it has its own tolerance range and, in many cases, could probably grow just as well or even better in another geographic location that provided a suitable environment. Almost all individuals have some degree of ability to grow in different environments even though in the adaptation they may change their appearance and, within limits, their physiology. These changes are phenotypic, of course, not genotypic.

Seldom does an individual plant grow isolated from the rest of its species. It is almost always a member of a group of other individuals of the same species, although this group may be somewhat isolated geographically or ecologically from the rest of the species. Almost all species are made up of a few to perhaps millions of these isolated or semi-isolated groups of individuals. Each group is a local population. Since almost all gene exchange between individuals occurs within the local population and since natural environmental selection sorts out the successful from the unsuccessful, the local population will eventually consist primarily of individuals adapted to the ranges of that particular environment. This is particularly true in cross-pollinating species in which the local populations are so isolated that gene exchange between populations is lacking or almost so. For these reasons, the interbreeding local population, rather than the individual itself, is the basic unit of evolution toward environmental fitness.

If plants or seeds from several local populations of a species are planted side by side in the homogeneous environment of a garden, almost invariably the individuals in a given population will differ to some extent from those of any other population. Almost all local populations, by the incorporation of successful mutations and hybrid combinations, have become genetically a little different from the rest of the species and, thus, specifically adapted to a certain environment.

This fact was first observed by Alexis Jordan in France as long ago as the 1860s. But because they appeared so different when grown side by side he named each population as a separate species. It was not until the early 1920s that Göte Turesson in Sweden, using the now classic technique of growing several local populations under identical conditions, established that local populations were really ecologically adapted genetic groups within a species. Turesson found that widespread species were not only made up of distinct local populations but that local populations of a species occurring in an environment such as the seacoast were similar to each other and distinct from local populations of the same species growing inland. A group of local populations from the same type of environment and showing similar inherited morphological characters, he called an "ecotype," today generally termed *ecological race*. An ecological race, then, is a group of local populations adapted to a given type of environment. While each local population within an ecological race varies somewhat from any other, they have greater similarities to each other than they do to populations from other ecological races in the same species.

Local populations and ecological races can be detected most easily by growing plants of a given species from various sources in a homogeneous environment. This can be a garden or a controlled environment room. Either transplants or seeds can be used; the latter have an advantage, however, in that they show more of the genetic range within a population.

The work of Turesson in Sweden and the work of Jens Clausen, William Hiesey, and David Keck in California have now demonstrated that almost every widespread species is made up of a complex of ecological races, which in turn are made up of local populations. Most of these conclusions have been based on growth and morphological differences as shown in uniform gardens, on observations of chromosomes, and on hybridization experiments. All of these demonstrate the basis of these ecological adaptations in genetic structure.

Evidence that the local populations of widespread species are physiologically different was first shown by Charles Olmsted, of the University of Chicago, who demonstrated that side-oats grama (*Bouteloua curtipendula*), a common American prairie grass, was made up of photoperiodic ecotypes; the populations from the Dakotas and Canada required longer days for flowering than did those from Texas and Arizona. Calvin McMillan of the University of Texas found that this same kind of photoperiodic variation occurs in several of the principal prairie grasses, and that it is coupled with a heat requirement that increases from north to south (from Canada to Texas) and from west to east (Wyoming to Iowa). Many of the prairie grasses flower first in the north in the long days of midsummer and later in the south during the shorter days of early autumn and after being exposed to thousands of hours of summer heat. The west-east gradient is an altitudinal gradient corresponding to the latitudinal north-south gradient. Grasses from the high plains of eastern Wyoming (7,000–8,000 ft above sea level) flower earlier and under the longer days of midsummer than plants of the same species in the lowland prairies of Iowa. This is a good thing for the Wyoming members of the species, for drought and winter come early on the high plains of the Laramie Basin.

The alpine sorrel (*Oxyria digyna*), the widespread arctic-alpine species discussed in Chapter 3, is also made up of photoperiodic races. All *Oxyria* plants remain dormant at a photoperiod of 12 hours. Those from California, Colorado, and Wyoming break dormancy and flower at about 15 hours. Usually, some of the plants in populations from near the Canadian–United States border will flower at 15 hours but many will not. None of the *Oxyria* plants from north of the Arctic Circle flowers at 15 hours. However, these arctic *Oxyrias* can be brought to flowering by very long photoperiods of over 20 hours.

Arctic *Oxyrias* also show other physiological differences from their alpine counterparts of lower latitudes. For example, they have more chlorophyll, higher respiration rates at the same temperatures, and reach peak photosynthesis at lower temperatures than alpine *Oxyrias*. Arctic *Oxyrias* that grow close to sea level are also not as efficient in using carbon dioxide in photosynthesis as their alpine relatives, which must operate in the thin atmosphere of the high mountains. *Oxyria* can grow in both arctic and alpine regions, which really are quite different kinds of environments, because it is made up of a series of ecological races which differ not only morphologically but physiologically. Most widespread species probably are made up of many ecological races or perhaps a genetic cline paralleling an environmental gradient. Since many ecological races combined with wide tolerance ranges in a given individual provide a very wide species tolerance range, it is safe to say that most of our weedy species have these characteristics. *Oxyria* has ecological races but any given *Oxyria* individual does not have a very wide tolerance range. It is restricted by its physiology to cold, snowy places with long enough summer photoperiods. Thus, it can never be an aggressive weed in the usual sense.

### Paleoecological Events and Present Distributions

Present distributions of most species cannot be completely explained on the basis of tolerance ranges alone. Young species may not yet have had time to spread. On the other hand, many species have been on earth for millions of years, as evidenced by the fossil record. In almost every case, the fossil distribution of the species is different from the distribution today—ample evidence that the distribution of most species is dynamic and constantly changing. A *paleoecological event* is any environmental change occurring in prehistoric times which had an effect on living organisms. Since only very marked effects are preserved in the fossil record, most paleoecological events of which we know anything were dramatic happenings such as the Pleistocene continental glaciation, the rise of mountains, severe climatic changes, and the rise of land from the sea or the converse.

The present distribution of most species is a product of the species' tolerance range, its ability and opportunity to cross barriers, the effects of paleoecological events, and time. The presence of a species in a place is ample evidence that the environment is suitable and that the species has been able to get there. The absence of a species from a place tells us nothing in itself, but presents a problem to be solved. It can be absent for one or more of several reasons: (1) the environment can be beyond the tolerance range; (2) barriers may have prevented the seeds from getting there; (3) it may once have been there but was eliminated by some paleoecological event. Interpretive ecological plant geography depends upon a synthesis of knowledge of many things (e.g., tolerance ranges, evolutionary history, ecological mobility, and the paleoecology of the species).

We get our knowledge of paleoecological events and past distributions from two main sources. First, from the fossil record left in mud or volcanic ash by leaves, fruits, seeds, and other plant parts, including wood which is often silicified (petrified). Second, from cores taken from lake and bog sediments and carefully analyzed inch by inch for preserved pollen and spores that can be identified at least to genus. By radioactive isotope dating, the approximate time at which the plant remains were preserved can be determined. Information derived from these two sources can be used not only to plot past distributions but, by using these plant fossils as climatic indicators, to get some idea of how climates have changed.

When European man arrived in North America in the latitude of Virginia, the vegetation consisted primarily of deciduous forests in the eastern third, grassland in the middle third, and a mixture of coniferous forests, chaparral, and deserts in the western third (see Fig. 4-2). Stretching across the Canadian part of the continent was (and still is) a vast belt of spruce-fir-pine forest, and north of that a belt of treeless arctic tundra. This, of course, is an oversimplification of a complex pattern that owes much of its complexity to the Cenozoic or Tertiary Era and the continental glaciations of the Pleistocene Epoch. Some of our best evidence for climatic and vegetational changes during the Cenozoic is from western North America and is largely the result of investigations by Professors Ralph W. Chaney and Daniel I. Axelrod of the University of California at Berkeley and Los Angeles, respectively. Most of the following discussion is based on their work.

At the beginning of the Tertiary, the continent was relatively low and relatively uncut by the many mountain ranges of today. There were only three main ranges: two in the Rocky Mountains, and one in the Appalachian region. Everything west of the present Utah-Nevada line was relatively low country with relatively even and mild climates. Tropical forests extended as far north as the state of Washington, and Alaska was covered with temperate forests of redwood and other species.

These warm and uniform conditions across the continent eventually came to a gradual close with volcanic activity and a cooling of the climate in Miocene times and ended in another great period of mountain building during the very late Pliocene and Pleistocene within the last million years or so. The gentle lands west of Utah were disrupted by great uplifting of rock to form the Sierra Nevada and the Basin Ranges of Nevada. The Cascade volcanoes came into action, building up great cones, while extensive lava flows were produced between the Cascade crest and the Rocky Mountains. The present Coast Ranges of California south of San Francisco and also the San Joaquin Valley were often submerged under the sea until after Miocene times.

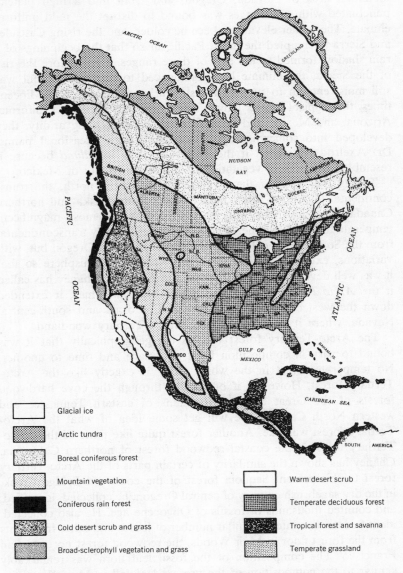

**Fig. 4-2.** *Diagrammatic map of the vegetational regions of North America at the time of settlement by European man.*

Legend:

- Glacial ice
- Arctic tundra
- Boreal coniferous forest
- Mountain vegetation
- Coniferous rain forest
- Cold desert scrub and grass
- Broad-sclerophyll vegetation and grass
- Warm desert scrub
- Temperate deciduous forest
- Tropical forest and savanna
- Temperate grassland

The formation of these mountains and the uplifting of the inter-mountain area of Nevada, Oregon, and Utah into a high plateau punctuated with new ranges was bound to disrupt the mild uniform climate. The higher elevations became colder, and the rising Cascades and Sierra intercepted the moist Pacific air so that the beginnings of a rain shadow formed to the east of these ranges. Even before the rise of the Sierra, the climate had commenced to turn cooler, but was still moist enough to support forest. During Oligocene and Miocene times, the tropical forests moved southward into southern California, Arizona, and Mexico and because of slowly increasing aridity, they developed into somewhat open woodlands with occasional palms. Dr. Axelrod has called it the *Madro-Tertiary woodland* because it resembled the present vegetation of the Sierra Madre of Mexico.

Taking the place of the tropical forests in the north, the trans-continental temperate forest moved down from Alaska and northern Canada. This northern Miocene forest was the most magnificent temperate forest of all time. It not only was essentially transcontinental from the Southern Appalachians to Washington and Oregon but, with variations, extended clear around the Northern Hemisphere so that it was well developed also in Europe and Asia. Dr. Chaney has called it the *Arcto-Tertiary forest*. In middle Miocene times, it extended down the west coast as far as central California and south-central Nevada, where it bordered on the Madro-Tertiary woodland.

The Arcto-Tertiary forest was so big geographically that it was bound to vary in composition from one place and time to another. No temperate forest in the world today is exactly like the Arcto-Tertiary forest. However, if one walks through the cove hardwood forests of the Great Smoky Mountains of eastern Tennessee and western North Carolina, he will get some idea of what the Arcto-Tertiary forest was like. Another forest quite like parts of the Arcto-Tertiary forest is the coastal redwood forest of northern California. Chaney has shown the similarity of certain parts of the Arcto-Tertiary forest to this present Sequoia forest of the coast. At Bridge Creek, in the dry sagebrush country of central Oregon, he collected, identified, and counted thousands of fossils of Oligocene age. He also collected, identified, and counted a similar number of leaves and other fragments from the forest floor in Muir Woods, the redwood forest north of San Francisco. The composition of the fossil leaf flora was remarkably similar to the composition of the present leaf fall in Muir Woods as to species and relative numbers. In the fossil flora were redwood, hemlock, alder, tan-oak, maple, dogwood, Oregon-myrtle, hazelnut, and many other species now present at Muir Woods. The conclusion is inescapable: during the Oligocene, about 27 million years ago, the vegetation and climate of central Oregon east of the present-day Cascades resembled that of the modern foggy northern California coast. No better evidence of climatic change and plant migration is needed.

There were places in the western part of the Arcto-Tertiary forest where genera were present that are now missing in western North America. In the Mascall fossil flora of central Oregon of Miocene age, in addition to the usual redwood, Oregon-myrtle, and alder, there were trees like sweet gum (*Liquidambar*), ginkgo (*Ginkgo biloba*), and *Grewia*. *Liquidambar* now is found only in the southeastern United States and eastern Asia, while *Ginkgo* and *Grewia* have been eliminated from North America entirely and occur now only in eastern Asia. Probably *Ginkgo* would be extinct today even in Asia if it had not been preserved as a sacred tree in temple gardens. Thus, in the last several million years as climates have changed and forest migrations have taken place, each species has reacted in its own way according to its own tolerance range. Although some of our present-day forests resemble certain parts of the Arcto-Tertiary forest, some species are missing and some others have been added.

Within the last million years or so, the climates of western North America began to turn much colder and drier. The mountains and valleys rose to even greater heights, and the Sierra and Cascades created a great rain shadow between their crests and the Rocky Mountains. Not only did the climate become colder and drier but the rainfall pattern changed. Instead of rainfall being evenly distributed throughout the year with plenty of summer rainfall, there was a shift toward winter precipitation and very little rain during the summer. This pattern persists today west of the Rocky Mountains.

These climatic changes had pronounced effects on the vegetation. The Arcto-Tertiary forest disappeared over much of its range, with remainders hanging on only in eastern North America and west of the Cascades and Sierra. The big-tree (*Sequoiadendron*), which had been a part of the Arcto-Tertiary forest in western Nevada, east of the Sierra, avoided extinction by migrating over the rising mountains before they became too high. It became established on the moister western side, where it remains today. Great grasslands, with herds of hoofed mammals such as the horse and camel, replaced the forest east of the Sierra and extended far into the interior of the continent. Pine, fir, and spruce forests covered the mountains. The land of Nevada, Idaho, and Utah began to resemble present-day Wyoming and Colorado but with less severe climate.

At the same time, because the disappearance of summer rain was most marked in the south and near the coast, the Madro-Tertiary flora retreated into the summer rain areas of the Sierra Madre of Mexico and southeastern Arizona. However, evolution in some species was rapid, and from some of these Madro-Tertiary species and perhaps some borderline Arcto-Tertiary species, came the California chaparral and live oak woodlands adapted to winter rain and long dry summers.

In late Pliocene and Pleistocene times, some 1 or 2 million years ago, with the Sierra rising rapidly, the climates became even more arid. From the retreating subtropical Madro-Tertiary flora, from the Arcto-Tertiary flora, and from the high mountains, new kinds of plants evolved that fitted these extremely dry conditions. Up to this time, there had been no real desert climate or desert vegetation in North America. The present deserts of the American Southwest owe their origin to increasing aridity in late Pliocene and Pleistocene times, and thus, compared to the forests, are recent phenomena. The species, and often the genera in them, are new. Since they have had little opportunity to spread, many of these species are endemic to the Southwest.

During this same period, in the eastern part of the continent, the Appalachians stayed low. The rains continued to come from the Gulf of Mexico, there was little aridity, and the moist Arcto-Tertiary forests remained with only minor changes.

Soon, however, things began to change rapidly. For some reason (and there are many theories), the snow that fell in winter in the north and in the mountains did not all melt the following summer. Every year there was more carry-over of old snow to the new winter, when even more snow fell. The winter snowfall increased, and permanent snowbanks in the mountains got larger and became more abundant. These snowbanks gradually turned to ice and because of their weight began to move down and away from the zone of accumulation. These events were the beginning of the Ice Age of the Pleistocene Epoch.

Four times the continental glaciers moved down past the middle of the continent east of the Rocky Mountains. In the West, four times mountain glaciers filled the old valleys and moved down into the lowlands, leaving only the high peaks and ridges exposed. Heavy precipitation built up great lakes in what had been the deserts and grasslands of Utah and Nevada. The western glaciers carved the mountains into new forms; the Tetons, the Beartooth, the Lewis Range, and many others emerged sharp and polished and devoid of much vegetation. In the eastern half of the continent, the ice stood a mile deep over Michigan and New York, and the Arcto-Tertiary forest was wiped out except in its Southern Appalachian and Mexican refuges. The spruce-fir-pine forest of the north was over-run, although many of its species migrated into Texas, the Gulf States, and the Carolinas. A thin strip of tundra may have remained just to the south of the glacial front, but the principal refuges for tundra plants in the East were the higher ridges and peaks of the Appalachians.

The climatic changes of the late Tertiary eradicated or restricted the Arcto-Tertiary and Madro-Tertiary vegetations of the West and aided the evolution of the floras of present deserts, chaparral, and pine forests. However, the eastern part of the forest probably escaped serious disruption until the Pleistocene ice. Nothing was more destructive than the physical mass of the ice and the severe climate to the south of the ice front. The land of the northeastern quarter of the United States and all of eastern Canada was either scoured away or covered with glacial debris; the vegetation was destroyed.

On a major scale, this destruction has occurred four times in the last million years. After each advance of the ice, warmer periods have followed, the ice has receded into the Arctic and the higher mountains, and the flora has migrated species by species both northward and upward. The last advance of the continental ice in eastern North America is known as the Wisconsin stage. This Wisconsin glaciation was so recent that it is possible to date its advances and retreats by the radioactivity of carbon-14 remaining in tree trunks and other organic debris over-run by the ice and left undecayed in the glacial deposits. Only 18,000 years ago, it was at its height, and its last minor advance down across the Lake States occurred only 11,000 years ago. Since that time, its retreat was fairly rapid except for one or two minor advances. All evidence appears to indicate that we are in another interglacial period.

The comings and goings of the ice naturally had marked effects on the vegetation and the distribution of species. Although there may have been a few isolated nonglaciated refuges in the north during certain times, almost all the vegetation of Michigan, for example, has migrated from the south during the last 11,000 years. Compared to the 60 million years of the Tertiary, this is almost no time at all. Primitive Indians followed the ice back and hunted down the hairy mammoths and other large mammals of the Pleistocene until they became extinct. These postglacial ecosystems were so near in time and yet so different from those today.

From the many excellent studies of pollen preserved in bogs and lake sediments of the Midwest, we have a good idea of how the vegetation migrated back and how long it took. For example, in Indiana there is a little bog named Bacon's Swamp, now surrounded by the city of Indianapolis. This bog originated about 15,000 years ago as a large block of ice left behind in the glacial gravels by the melting Wisconsin continental ice sheet. The block of ice soon melted into a small lake surrounded by bare gravels and sands. It was a bleak, treeless landscape with perhaps a few scattered hardy plants. Only a relatively few miles to the south was the northern boundary of the spruce-fir forest. Seeds of these trees eventually reached the margins of the little lake and germinated, and in a century or two the lake was surrounded by a dark, cold forest. Every year, the trees released their characteristic pollen, some of which blew into the lake and was preserved in the cold, acid peat that gradually filled the lake as the Sphagnum moss and sedges formed a floating mat over its surface. From cores of peat or lake sediments, such pollen can be washed out and identified to genus and sometimes even to species.

Century after century the climate grew warmer as the ice front retreated farther away. Then white pine and hemlock moved northward from their southern refuges. The forest gradually changed, with spruce and fir disappearing from central Indiana and moving northward. A few oaks appeared, and some maples, elms, and beech. The forest took on the character of what we might call today "northern hardwood forest." But the climate warmed up very rapidly and the rainfall amounts decreased. This relatively warm, arid period reached a peak only about 5,000 years ago. The trees died out except for scattered groves, and the prairie grasses moved in from the west. Buffalo roamed the prairies; central Indiana resembled preagricultural Illinois or even Kansas.

Finally, the rains returned and the environment again became moist enough for forest. Oak, maple, and beech reappeared, but this time they were joined by some old Arcto-Tertiary trees from the southern Appalachian refuge: tulip trees (*Liriodendron*), walnuts (*Juglans*), pawpaws (*Asimina*), and hickories (*Carya*). The forest became richer in species and had a greater resemblance to the old Tertiary forest. Even today the northward migration continues, with trees such as sweet gum (*Liquidambar*) and persimmon (*Diospyros*) being recent arrivals. Bacon's Swamp is now almost filled in, houses fill the forest, and the cycle has been broken by man—at least for this interglacial period. Similar paleoecological evidence is available from many other eastern American bogs and lakes.

The major effect of this Tertiary and Pleistocene climatic and glacial activity has been migration and evolution in almost every genus of vascular plants that existed in North America at the beginning of the Tertiary. Many such as *Ginkgo* were completely destroyed on this continent. Others such as the redwood of the California coast retreated to refuges where local climates have helped them to survive; but they remain in these refuges unable to escape because of relatively new climatic and geographic barriers. Still other species, such as the boreal white spruce, migrated southward into the lowlands of the Piedmont, the Coastal Plain, and even Texas, and then moved rapidly back northward following the ice, so that today white spruce stretches across Canada and Alaska from the Atlantic to the Pacific.

Increasing aridity in the region between the Sierra Nevada and the Mississippi River has produced a distinct kind of discontinuous distribution pattern in some of the old transcontinental Arcto-Tertiary species. This disruption broke many genera into two groups: one on the Pacific Coast, west of the Sierran-Cascade axis, and another east of the Mississippi River. In some cases, such as *Liquidambar* (sweet gum) and *Carpinus* (hornbeam), the western group was eliminated by aridity, cold, or both. The single American species remaining in each genus (*Liquidambar* and *Carpinus*) is now restricted to the eastern deciduous forest, where each is widespread and vigorous. In other cases, the separation into two non–gene-exchanging groups has allowed the evolution of two or more closely related but geographically isolated species from a common Arcto-Tertiary ancestor. One of these species is in California and one or more in the eastern forests. Examples are the redbud, *Cercis canadensis,* in the East, and *Cercis occidentalis* in the West; the sweetshrub, *Calycanthus floridus* in the East, and *Calycanthus occidentalis* in the West; the eastern and western poison oaks, *Rhus quercifolia* in the East, and *Rhus diversiloba* in California.

The settler from the East who came slowly and painfully across the plains and deserts in his covered wagon in 1850 on arriving in California found many new and strange plants but also many familiar plants, even though they were slightly different from those at home. The strange ones were those that had evolved from various sources as the California climate became arid at the end of the Pliocene and returned to aridity after the Pleistocene; the familiar plants were those that remained as survivors of the old transcontinental Tertiary forests.

# 5

# STRUCTURE AND
# CLASSIFICATION
# OF PLANT
# COMMUNITIES

Genetically, individuals are members of their local populations; ecologically, they are members of an ecosystem. The greatest part of an ecosystem consists of the plants or vegetation. This part of an ecosystem can be called a *plant community*.

## COMMUNITY STRUCTURE AND SAMPLING

The individuals of various species in a plant community are not distributed in merely a hit or miss fashion. The distribution of seeds, microenvironmental patterns, and the sizes and kinds of other plants all interact to produce definite patterns of individuals and species in the community. Plant communities range in complexity from single-layered communities of a single species, such as that of desert salt-grass or a clean crop of corn, to the multilayered and complex tropical rain forest.

Either from the viewpoint of the ecology of component species or from the viewpoint of understanding the ecology of the whole ecosystem, we need to know how the individuals and populations of each species are distributed in the community. We also must know their numbers and the structure of the whole community in terms of the population structure of each component species.

To describe a plant community, we first must describe the plants physically and give each kind a name. In other words, the community is described in both physiognomic and floristic terms. For example, to describe the structure of a nearby woods, we would first walk through the woods several times and make a complete list of the species of plants that are there. While making this list, we might also classify each species by some physiognomic or life-form system. For example, this could mean designating each species in the woods as belonging to one of the following life-form classes:

| | |
|---|---|
| Dominant or overstory tree | Low shrub |
| Secondary or understory tree | Perennial herb |
| Seedling tree | Annual herb |
| Tall shrub | Moss or lichen |

Of course, we could break up this simple life-form system into more precise groups, but this is sufficient for most vegetational descriptions.

While making this preliminary survey of the woods, we would immediately see that the vegetation has a vertical structure or pattern. The vertical structure is usually made up of distinct strata, the size and number of which depend upon the kinds of life forms present. Most temperate forest communities are composed of at least three or four strata. The upper stratum consists of relatively large overstory trees, which dominate the community by shading and, therefore, determine the number of other strata and kinds of plants composing these lower strata. Below these taller trees, there is usually a stratum consisting of the crowns of secondary or understory trees. These secondary trees are relatively tolerant of shading and normally do not grow nearly as tall as the dominants. Below the secondary trees will usually be one or more strata of shrubs, and below and between the shrubs will be one or more layers of herbaceous plants. Mosses or lichens may be common as a low layer on the ground, or they may be absent. Tree seedlings and saplings of either the dominant or understory species may appear in any of the lower strata as they pass up through on their way to maturity.

Some desert, alpine, or grassland communities may have fewer strata, or they may have on a miniature scale an even more elaborate vertical structure. Tropical rain forests, on the other hand, are extremely complex vertically and have several layers of trees, with epiphytes such as orchids perched high in the crowns where there is light and vines (lianas) hanging down like ropes. The diagrammatic vertical profiles through tropical rain forest, temperate forest, and desert are contrasted in Fig. 5-1.

Vertical structure is largely due to the effects of diminishing light and increasing humidity downward; horizontal or areal structure, on the other hand, is due to the interaction of so many factors that it is much more complex and difficult to see. Although the individuals of each species in the community are distributed according to their respective tolerance ranges, competition between individuals of several species for the same environmental space results in complex patterns

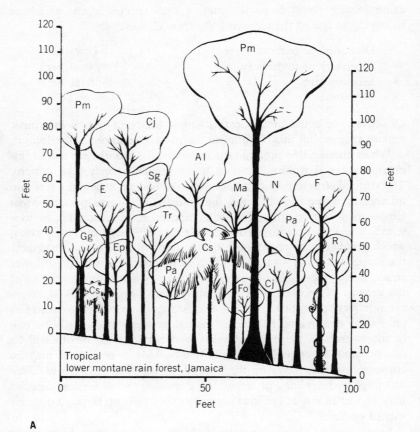

A

of distribution. In general, any one species in a given community will have one of the three following distribution patterns: *regular,* as trees in an orchard; *irregular,* clumped all in one place; or *randomly scattered* throughout the community.

We should also like to know the relative amount of ground covered by the foliage of each species. Cover values are rough measures of the degree of dominance of a species in its stratum. In simple communities or in rapid surveys, we could make rough estimates of relative abundance and relative coverage of the common species by walking through the vegetation. But such estimates can be quite erroneous and misleading unless done by someone very experienced in that vegetation type. By the nature of the subject, it is almost impossible to describe adequately the areal composition of a plant community in

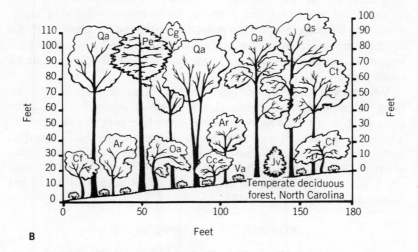

B

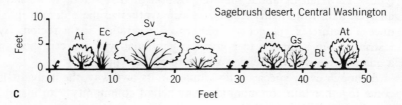

C

**Fig. 5-1.** *Diagrammatic profiles through tropical rain forest (Jamaica, from Asprey and Robbins, 1953), temperate deciduous forest (North Carolina), and cold desert vegetation (Washington state).*

## Key to species

**A. Rain forest:** Al, *Alchornia latifolia* (jumba); Cj, *Calophyllum jacquinii* (Santa Maria); Cs, *Calyptronoma swartzii;* E, *Eugenia* sp. (rodwood); Ep, *Exothea paniculata* (wild ginep); F, *Ficus* sp.; Fo, *Faramea occidentalis* (wild coffee); Gg, *Guarea glabra* (alligator, wild akee); Ma, *Matayba apetala* (wannika); N, *Nectandra* sp. (sweetwood); Pa, *Pithecellobium alexandrii* (shadbark); Pm, *Psidium montanum* (mountain guava); R, Rubiaceous sp.; Sg, *Symphonia globulifera* (hog gum); Tr, *Trophis racemosa* (ramoon).

**B. Temperate forest:** Ar, *Acer rubrum* (red maple); Cc, *Cercis canadensis* (redbud); Cf, *Cornus florida* (dogwood); Cg, *Carya glabra* (pignut hickory); Ct, *Carya tomentosa* (mockernut hickory); Jv, *Juniperus virginiana* (red cedar); Oa, *Oxydendrum arboreum* (sourwood); Pe, *Pinus echinata* (shortleaf pine); Qa, *Quercus alba* (white oak); Qs, *Quercus stellata* (post oak); Va, *Viburnum affine* (arrow-wood).

**C. Cold desert:** At, *Artemisia tridentata* (sagebrush); Bt, *Bromus tectorum* (cheatgrass); Ec, *Elymus cinereus* (giant wild-rye); Gs, *Grayia spinosa* (hopsage); Sv, *Sarcobatus vermiculatus* (greasewood).

qualitative terms. Some form of quantitative sampling should be used.

There are three principal methods for sampling vegetation quantitatively: by plots, by plotless point methods, and by transects.* All of these are based upon mathematical statistics and are used in attempts to describe the structure of the whole vegetation by sampling a small portion.

Vegetational sampling methods are still being developed; no sampling method has yet appeared that gives a completely adequate picture of every kind of vegetation. Sampling procedures must be adapted to the kind of vegetation being sampled, to the time allowable, and to the completeness desired. The only perfect way of describing a woods would be to count, measure, identify, and locate by map every individual in it; obviously, very few of us have the time or patience to do this.

## COMMUNITY CLASSIFICATION

Data obtained from a single stand of vegetation are termed "analytic." They tell us about the composition of that stand. If we have analytic data from many stands, we can synthesize these data to produce a picture of the general pattern of vegetation for a region. By restricting our sampling to a given vegetational type, we can show in a quantitative way the general structure of the type.

Although every species is distributed in its own way, the individuals come together into communities. Any actual community with natural or arbitrary limits is called a *stand*. A stand is real; one can see it or walk into it. Anyone who has sampled much vegetation knows that no two stands are exactly alike. However, some stands resemble each other much more than they resemble other stands. We can classify stands that have certain things in common into vegetational types or associations. This is done by ecologists, plant sociologists, foresters, and range-management people. A loblolly pine type or association in North Carolina, for example, has certain characteristics quite different from those of a post oak–blackjack oak type. All loblolly pine stands, though each is slightly different, will resemble each other in composition more than they will resemble a post oak–blackjack oak stand. If a loblolly pine stand is adjacent to a post oak–blackjack oak stand, the *ecotone* or boundary zone between them will be quite sharp, and one can almost step across it. The same thing would be true for the eco-

*The subject of vegetation sampling is too technical and specialized to take up in detail here. For more information, the reader may consult the following: Cain and Castro (1959), Greig-Smith (1957), Oosting (1956), and Phillips (1959).

tones determined by contrasting rock types in California or Nevada.

Vegetational mapping requires the recognition of some system of types or associations and the marking of boundaries on the map. Where communities are distinct and have sharp ecotones, they are easy to classify into types, and also to map. Where environmental gradients are gradual and ecotones are blurred or wide, vegetational mapping is more difficult. Here it may be necessary to recognize a vegetational continuum, a pattern that shifts along a directional gradient in such a way that strictly comparable community types are not repeated and yet neither are two stands too unlike. Perhaps it is all a matter of how arbitrary we are in setting up vegetational types. Even if continua are recognized, it is still possible to map them in some way.

Mapping of actual vegetation or the vegetational potential of a region is of great practical importance. Forest-type maps, range-type maps, and general vegetational maps are in wide use by many kinds of investigators. European countries are almost all completely mapped vegetationally on large-scale maps. Very little of the United States is so mapped.

Mapping, of course, presupposes some degree of classification. The mapper must be familiar with the general vegetation and the repetition of types. He must also be able to recognize the ecotones and use them as his map boundaries if the ecotones are narrow, or to map them as continuum-type communities if the ecotones are broad.

Before a region can be mapped, its vegetation should be fairly well known. However, since some mapping is better than none, it is not necessary to wait until every stand is analyzed—this will never be. Mapping requires good ground reconnaissance and recognition of vegetational types. Mapping is also greatly facilitated by modern methods of aerial photography. Modern aerial cameras and certain kinds of films such as infrared film can detect many differences not only between stands of different types but also between species and between healthy trees and diseased trees. With these techniques vegetational mapping is now proceeding rapidly, and we soon shall know more of worldwide vegetational structure and distribution.

# 6

# ECOSYSTEM
# DYNAMICS

Vegetation has three main roles in an ecosystem. First, vegetation is the great modifier of environment: it cuts down solar radiation, minimizes temperature extremes, transfers moisture from the soil to the air by transpiration, adds humus to the soil, and in hundreds of other ways changes the environment. Thus, it indirectly determines the kinds of organisms that can live in the ecosystem.

Second, and even more important, vegetation is the energy fixer for the whole ecosystem. The energy of solar radiation is useless to animals (except for temporary warmth) until it is captured by the chlorophyll of vegetation and converted into the chemical energy of food molecules upon whose energy-rich bonds all organisms can draw. The living parts of ecosystems run on this energy; they could not exist without photosynthesis of green vegetation.

The third role of vegetation is just as important. Life requires carbon, hydrogen, oxygen, nitrogen, calcium, and many other elements. These elements exist principally in the soil, either temporarily or permanently, or in the atmosphere. Animals and people have no easy means of freeing and absorbing the mineral molecules and ions from the soil. Nor can they synthesize these inorganic molecules into basic protoplasmic compounds such as essential amino acids, the building blocks of proteins. The vegetation, then, is the source of almost all necessary minerals used by the living organisms of an ecosystem. Finally, vegetation, by photosynthesis and respiration, plays a fundamental role in the cycling of oxygen and carbon.

## ENERGY FLOW THROUGH THE ECOSYSTEM

Most of the solar radiation falling on vegetation and soil is reflected, used in evapotranspiration, or used in raising soil, plant, and air temperatures. This energy returns eventually to space as long wavelengths of infrared, and thus the heat balance of the earth is maintained. Only about 1 per cent or less of the energy in solar radiation is actually absorbed in the photosynthetic process and enters the living part of the ecosystem. This relatively small amount, however, is enough to support the mass of life in a tropical rain forest or in the ocean. It is also enough to produce 100 bushels of corn seed per acre on an Illinois farm, not counting the corn plants themselves, or the mice, birds, insects, fungi, and bacteria that live off the corn. Since it "wastes" 99 per cent of the energy, vegetation seems at first glance like a rather inefficient engine for transferring energy into the ecosystem; however, its actual output is rather good, especially under intensive management. A. G. Norman of the University of Michigan has calculated that, to produce the 100 bushels of corn per acre, about 20,000 pounds of carbon dioxide are needed. Since carbon dioxide makes up such a small proportion of the atmosphere, the corn plants on one acre must "process" about 21,000 tons of air to get this carbon dioxide! Certainly this could be called efficient.

What would happen if we could double the light-absorbing efficiency of the photosynthetic process? In such a case, the principle of limiting factors would come into action very quickly. As illustrated by the corn–carbon dioxide example, the yield of organisms per acre is determined not just by the efficiency of light absorption but by available water, carbon dioxide, temperature, nitrogen, phosphorus, and many other environmental components. Efficiency of energy fixation is governed by the ability of a plant to manufacture food in the presence of a limiting factor. Although this limiting factor can be light, it is often something else. There is plenty of light in the Gila River desert of Arizona but an unirrigated spruce tree would not be efficient there; in fact, it would die. The creosote bush (*Larrea*), on the other hand, does well in the face of a limiting factor such as drought, and is considerably more efficient than the spruce in that environment. If the creosote bush were put in the subalpine zone of the Rocky Mountains, where temperature is limiting, it could not compete with the spruce in efficiency of food production. In short, efficiency of energy fixation by vegetation is not just a matter of what percentage of the available light energy is fixed but how much is fixed under the impact of whatever factor is limiting, whether carbon dioxide, water, phosphorus, temperature, or light itself.

The *productivity* of an ecosystem is the rate at which solar energy is fixed by the vegetation. Gross productivity is equal to the rate of photosynthesis. In growth and photosynthesis, however, plants utilize food that is not passed on to animals or fungi. Hence, net productivity of the vegetation—that productivity which in theory can be utilized by other organisms—is equal to the rate of photosynthesis (dry-matter production) minus the rate of plant respiration. Because temperature and light vary through the 24-hour cycle, these rates, in order to be meaningful, would have to be stated in terms of milligrams of carbon dioxide made into food per gram of leaf dry weight per 24 hours. Since this would necessitate rather delicate measurements, it could be stated in larger units such as grams of dry weight produced per unit area of land surface per growing season or per year.

For example, the net productivity of the above-ground parts of alpine tundra vegetation (Bliss, 1962) ranges between 0.5 and 4 grams dry weight per square meter per day if based on a growing season of 60–70 days. If based on the entire year, the productivity would range only from about 0.06 to 0.6 grams per meter$^2$ per day. The low rate on a yearly basis is due to the fact that the vegetation in alpine ecosystems is only active photosynthetically for about two months a year. If roots and rhizomes are also included in these figures for alpine tundra, the net productivity figures are just about tripled (Scott and Billings, 1964). A tropical ecosystem with no cold season would be much more productive on a yearly basis, perhaps of the order of 15 grams per meter$^2$ per day; but since the entire year is the growing season, the relative efficiencies of the two systems in utilizing their environments would have to be based on the growing-season figures.

There are two general ways to measure productivity. First, samples of the vegetation can be harvested on an area basis from time to time during the growing season, dried, and weighed. This will give the rate at which dry matter is produced per unit area. Usually this is done by simply clipping off the shoots of plants at ground level from several typical sample plots at stated intervals. Since the roots are often ignored, this gives only the net productivity of the shoots. Such figures are not really complete enough to measure the total energy available to the ecosystem since many animals eat roots and rhizomes, and fungi and bacteria also live on them. If possible, then, the harvest method of productivity measurement should include sampling of the weight increase of roots also. Productivity data are even more valuable if measurements are made of caloric content and digestibility of the dry matter produced.

The second method, easier and more elegant, is to measure the rates of photosynthesis and respiration of whole plants or unit areas of sod including roots by some instrument that measures uptake or output of carbon dioxide or oxygen per unit time. Such a recording instrument can be used in the laboratory under controlled conditions or in the field under natural conditions. The most widely used instrument of this type at present is the infrared gas analyzer (Fig. 6-1),

**Fig. 6-1.** *Use of an infrared gas analyzer in measuring photosynthesis and respiration rates under field conditions in the alpine tundra of the Medicine Bow Mountains, Wyoming.*

which can detect carbon dioxide in very small amounts in an airstream and thus measure and record the amount used in photosynthesis or produced in respiration in a given amount of time.

The total dry weight of organisms per unit area in an ecosystem is called the *biomass*. The biomass existing in the system at any given time is the *standing crop*. The amount of new biomass produced in a single growing season is known as the *yield*. In order to understand the operation and efficiency of an ecosystem, we need to subdivide the standing crop into different energy levels or steps in the food chain.

A *food chain* is simply the series of kinds of organisms through which food energy moves. For example, red clover plants in a meadow produce food, a field mouse eats the clover and thus gets food, a weasel eats the field mouse and gets his food, and perhaps still another carnivore such as an eagle eats the weasel. Food energy moves up the food chain from clover to eagle. Each level in the food chain is called a *trophic level* or *energy level*. In the example just given, the clover vegetation is at trophic level 1 $(T_1)$, or the producing level; all other levels above this are consuming levels. The field mouse is a part of $T_2$, the herbivore level. The weasel is at $T_3$, the carnivore level; and the eagle is at $T_4$, the top carnivore level. There are often no sharp lines between carnivore and top carnivore levels since the eagle too might eat the mouse. The fifth trophic level gets its energy from any of the first four levels. This level is made up of the decomposers—that is, fungi and bacteria.

In any balanced ecosystem, the standing crops at each trophic level have a definite relationship to each other. By far the greatest weight of organisms is in the producer $T_1$, the vegetation. Vegetation forms the base of a biomass pyramid in which the biomass of each successive trophic level above is smaller. The only exception is the weight of the decomposers in $T_5$, which is large because it can draw on all four of the other trophic levels.

Figure 6-2 is a schematic diagram of energy content and energy flow through a typical ecosystem. Note that there is energy loss by respiration at every trophic level. Therefore, there is a reduction at every trophic level in the amount of food energy available to the trophic level above. Nevertheless, not all of this food is actually utilized by the next trophic level; some is left to the decomposers. Eventually, of course, all the energy absorbed as light in photosynthesis returns to the environment as heat energy at the various trophic levels and is radiated into space.

## MINERAL CYCLING THROUGH THE ECOSYSTEM

The source of the necessary mineral elements in a terrestrial ecosystem is the soil. These elements get into the biological part of the ecosystem through absorption by the roots of vascular plants or by fixation by soil microorganisms. Certain mineral elements (e.g., phosphorus and nitrogen) may be in short supply in some ecosystems. In such cases, almost all of the supply of these elements in the ecosystem will be tied up in the organic part of the system. The lack of the element then becomes limiting to the productivity of the system. Just as the ecosystem will not run without solar energy being fixed by the green plants, neither will this energy be carried through the system nor will the organisms grow without the necessary minerals being made available by plants.

A familiar mineral cycle is that of nitrogen. The greater part of the earth's atmosphere is gaseous nitrogen and this is the main reservoir of the cycle. Since nitrogen as a gas is relatively inert, most organisms cannot make use of it as a nutrient. However, there are a few kinds of microorganisms (certain species of bacteria, some blue-green algae) that are able to utilize gaseous nitrogen from the soil atmosphere. Almost all of the nitrogen that leaves the atmospheric reservoir does so through these small soil organisms, which fix or reduce molec-

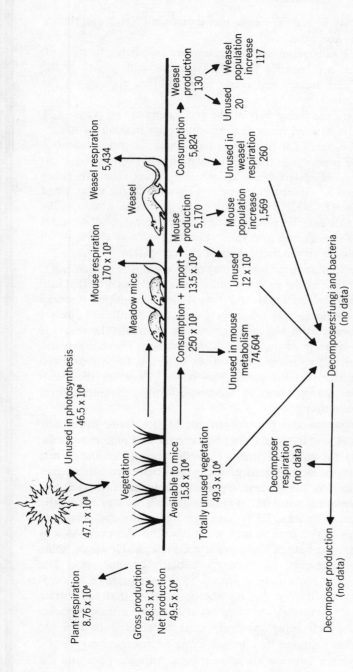

**Fig. 6-2.** *Diagram of energy flow through the principal food chain of an abandoned field ecosystem in Michigan. Vegetation was dominated principally by Canada blue-grass (Poa compressa), the principal vertebrate herbivore was the meadow mouse (Microtus pennsylvanicus), and one of the main predators or carnivores was the least weasel (Mustela rixosa). Figures are in kilogram-calories per hectare. Data from Golley (1960).*

Sun $47.1 \times 10^8$

Unused in photosynthesis $46.5 \times 10^8$

Plant respiration $8.76 \times 10^6$

Gross production $58.3 \times 10^6$

Net production $49.5 \times 10^6$

Vegetation

Available to mice $15.8 \times 10^6$

Totally unused vegetation $49.3 \times 10^6$

Meadow mice

Mouse respiration $170 \times 10^3$

Consumption + import $250 \times 10^3$ $13.5 \times 10^3$

Unused in mouse metabolism 74,604

Mouse production 5,170

Unused $12 \times 10^3$

Mouse population increase 1,569

Weasel

Weasel respiration 5,434

Consumption 5,824

Unused in weasel respiration 260

Weasel production 130

Unused 20

Weasel population increase 117

Decomposers:fungi and bacteria (no data)

Decomposer respiration (no data)

Decomposer production (no data)

ular nitrogen ($N_2$) within their cells into ammonia ($NH_3$) and thence into amino acids and proteins.

Many of these nitrogen-fixing organisms are free-living in the soil. Others, however, are bacteria that are symbiotic with plants of the legume family and alders, and occur in prominent nodules on the roots of these plants.

Nitrogen enters the living part of the ecosystem in two ways: (1) "new" nitrogen is derived from the atmosphere by fixation by microorganisms; (2) nitrates (or sometimes ammonia), already present in the soil as cyclic products in the decomposition and eventual nitrification of dead organic material, are absorbed by plant roots. In either case, the nitrogen is reduced in the microorganism or the green plant to amino groups ($R–NH_2$), which are parts of certain amino acids. These amino acids are the precursors or components of all nitrogen compounds in the organism and thus, through the food chain, of all nitrogen compounds in the living part of the ecosystem.

Upon the death of an organism or part of an organism (e.g., a leaf), the reduced nitrogen of the proteins and nucleic acids is converted into ammonia ($NH_3$) by bacterial and fungal decomposition. A small amount of this ammonia may enter plant roots and be utilized directly in the metabolism of the higher plants. Most ammonia, however, is utilized by soil bacteria of the genus *Nitrosomonas*. These organisms oxidize the ammonia to nitrite. The nitrite in turn is further oxidized to nitrate by bacteria of the genus *Nitrobacter*. Together these two steps that change nitrogen from the ammonia form to the nitrate form are called "nitrification."

Both higher plants and microorganisms reduce these bacterially produced nitrates within their cells to ammonia and amino radicals, thus completing the nitrogen cycle. However, not all of the nitrate nitrogen stays in the organic part of the cycle—there are two sources of loss. First, nitrate, being very soluble, tends to be leached out of the soil by percolating rainwater. This nitrate finds its way eventually into ground water, streams, lakes, and eventually into the oceans or inland salt lakes. Even here it may remain within the cycle as it is utilized by algae, the base of the aquatic food chains. However, some is lost to deep sediments, which may eventually become rock. The second loss is more immediate; it occurs to the atmosphere by denitrification of nitrate by certain soil microorganisms that use nitrate as a substitute for oxygen. Denitrification reduces the nitrate to molecular nitrogen, which being relatively inert becomes a part of the atmosphere unless captured by nitrogen-fixing microorganisms.

Thus, the bridges between the atmospheric nitrogen pool and the organic nitrogen pool are made up of microorganisms that either reduce nitrate to gaseous nitrogen or fix the latter into organic compounds. If the cycle is to remain in balance, the activity of one group should not exceed the activity of the other. Biological activity on earth would gradually decrease if the rate of loss of nitrogen to the atmosphere caused by the "denitrifiers" exceeded the rate of capture of nitrogen by the "fixers." However, the system is eventually self-correcting in that a decrease in fixation would eventually result in a decrease in the available nitrogenous substratum for the denitrifying organisms. The time necessary for the attainment of a new balance, however, would probably be quite great.

Minerals such as phosphorus do not cycle readily. The primary source of most phosphorus is the apatite group of minerals (principally calcium fluophosphate). However, most of the phosphorus in an ecosystem is derived from the breakdown of dead organic material. The phosphate anion has a strong affinity for certain kinds of clay particles such as kaolinite. It may be so tightly bound by the kaolinite that even though the soil may contain considerable phosphorus, only a small amount is available for absorption by roots. This is the reason that phosphate fertilizers must be applied in rather heavy doses if phosphate is limiting in crop or pasture land, as it so frequently is. In some tropical forests where kaolinite is the principal clay in the red lateritic soil, much of the available phosphorus may be tied up in the living biomass or in the trunks of the trees. Erosion removes phosphorus tightly bound in the clay particles from terrestrial environments. When these clays are deposited as sediments in lakes or in the ocean, the phosphorus may be out of circulation for millions of years.

Other elements such as sulfur, calcium, magnesium, and potassium move through the ecosystem after absorption by plants and, like phosphorus, are returned to the soil by decomposers working on the dead litter under trees or grass. Individuals of some plant species tend to concentrate certain elements in their leaves. Beech, dogwood, and eastern red cedar, for example, concentrate calcium, and their litter is thus rich in calcium. The breakdown of such litter returns calcium to the surface soil, where it becomes available to the roots of other plants. Some kinds of trees concentrate relatively rare elements such as copper or zinc in their leaves. These elements, of course, are necessary in small amounts in the metabolism of all organisms, but such heavy concentrations are unusual. The decomposition of leaf litter under these trees adds large amounts of these trace elements to the surface soil.

With certain radioactive isotopes becoming more abundant in the environment, it is becoming imperative that we know more about the absorption and cycling of minerals in the ecosystem, and at what rates. It is important to know, for example, the pathways by which potassium 40 and strontium 90 get into bones and teeth. Ecologists have found that Eskimos in certain Alaskan villages now have unusually high whole-body counts of cesium 137. These people subsist largely on caribou, which also have shown a recent increase in cesium 137. The source of the isotope is fallout from atomic testing which falls to earth with rain and snow and is absorbed by many kinds of arctic lichens. Caribou feed on the lichens, Eskimos eat the caribou, and the radioactive isotope is concentrated in their bodies.

## CYCLING OF GASES IN THE ECOSYSTEM

There are two principal cycles involving gases in the ecosystem. One is the nitrogen cycle, which is also involved as a part of mineral cycling. The second is the oxygen-carbon–dioxide-water cycle. This cycle is based upon the use, by all but anaerobic organisms, of gaseous oxygen in respiration. In respiration, of course, the net exchange results in the freeing of carbon dioxide and water. As will be remembered, these are the raw materials of photosynthesis. While very little of the water used in photosynthesis probably comes directly from respiration, carbon dioxide is a relatively rare gas in the atmosphere and its carbon is necessary as a component for all food. If the respiration of all organisms, particularly that of the decomposer microorganisms, were to stop, much of the available carbon would be tied up in dead material, and photosynthesis rates would slow down. However, man is inadvertently increasing the carbon dioxide content of the air by burning fossil fuels such as coal and oil in which the carbon was fixed by photosynthesis millions of years ago. Thus, where carbon dioxide may have been a limiting factor in ecosystem productivity, such productivity may eventually increase.

Since gaseous oxygen is being used up continually in ecosystem respiration, it would be depleted rapidly without the replenishment of oxygen in photosynthesis. Evidence indicates that this new oxygen is derived not from the separation of the carbon and oxygen in carbon dioxide but by the splitting apart of hydrogen and oxygen in water molecules during a part of photosynthesis. No other natural process in the ecosystem can break down an abundant compound such as water and provide enough oxygen to keep atmospheric levels close to the 21 per cent to which terrestrial organisms are adapted. So, again, we have evidence of the basic function of green vegetation in keeping the earth's ecosystems from running down.

## INTERACTIONS BETWEEN ORGANISMS IN THE ECOSYSTEM

One of the principal interactions between plants and animals in the ecosystem is the eating of some part of the vegetation by the animals. In this sense, all animals, including man, are parasites of green plants. But in the many million years of ecosystem evolution, some intricate and fascinating symbiotic relationships between animals and plants have developed. Many of these are involved with pollination and seed dispersal. Some relationships are of advantage to the plants because they allow interchange of genes with distant individuals of the same species without too much loss of pollen. Other symbiotic relationships are involved in the carrying of seeds into new and favorable locations for germination.

Many plants are insect-pollinated, with the insect gaining food from pollen and nectar. The elaborate structures developed both in flowers and in insects to aid this pollination are among the most amazing examples of symbiotic evolution. Each of the thousands of species of tropical orchids has an elaborate way of attracting pollinating insects. Plants of the genus *Yucca* (Spanish bayonet, Joshua tree, etc.) in North America are completely dependent upon moths of the genus *Pronuba* (*Tegeticula*) for pollination. The moth actually puts the pollen on the stigma of the pistil, then lays its eggs in the ovary of the flower. The developing larvae use some of the seeds for food, but not all, for the elimination of *Yucca* seeds would also eliminate *Pronuba*.

Many fleshy-fruited plants depend on birds for the dispersal of their seeds. The fact that red cedar trees (*Juniperus virginiana*) often grow in rows across old pastures in West Virginia or North Carolina is not accidental; there is or was a perchable fence that determined this unilateral distribution.

Interactions between plants are more difficult to see. There are parasitic reactions between many fungi and the higher plants causing plant diseases. There are even higher plants such as *Orobanche* or *Epifagus* which exist as parasites on the roots of sagebrush or trees and can therefore live without green leaves. Throughout the wet tropics there are various species of strangler figs (*Ficus*) which do not act as parasites for food but for space. These figs germinate high in the branches of the host tree and send down twining roots around the trunk of the host and leafy branches into the crown. Eventually, the original tree dies and is replaced by a fig tree firmly rooted in the ground and with its crown occupying its stolen canopy space.

There are symbiotic relationships among the higher plants principally through the effects that different plants have on the environment. The symbiotic relationships between certain algae and fungi which produce the lichen form of ecosystem are well known.

In most ecosystems the principal interaction between plants is *competition*. Competition results when one plant individual interferes with the needs of another individual for light, water, minerals, or any other necessary environmental commodity. Except for the direct approach of the strangler fig or the biochemical suppression of herbs by certain kinds of shrubs, competition is almost always exerted indirectly through effects on environmental components. However, the indirect approach is very effective since in any given environment there is only so much light or water. Individual plants weaken or die, populations disappear, and the nature of the vegetation changes. Competition is most severe between plants having similar life forms and environmental requirements, whether or not they are closely related.

Actually, in certain species there may also be cooperation of a sort between members of a local population. F. H. Bormann and B. F. Graham at Dartmouth College found in stands of eastern white pine (*Pinus strobus*) in New England that root grafting was quite common between the trees. Dyes or radioisotopes such as phosphorus 32 injected into one individual would appear in another. This transfer through roots could indicate a sharing of the mineral and water resources by near relatives in the vegetation. It would not be surprising to find a similar phenomenon in the uniform aspen stands (*Populus tremuloides*) of the western American mountains.

## VEGETATIONAL CHANGE AND STABILITY

We all know what happens when we fail to cultivate or weed the garden; weeds soon replace the tomatoes or marigolds. On a small scale, this replacement is similar to the change that takes place in the vegetation of any ecosystem where a limiting factor is removed. Moreover, the dominant plants of an ecosystem may so change the microenvironment that their reproduction fails, whereas that of another species with different tolerances will succeed.

In the case of the garden, the limiting factor for weeds is selective cultivation. When this is removed, the weeds' ever abundant seedlings survive and soon overtop the cultivated plants. If we should decide to abandon this garden completely, would the weeds remain there year after year? Part of the answer depends on the geographic location and available seed sources. However, in most cases, there will be a change in vegetation from the weeds to something else. The change may be either gradual or fast, and will continue until the vegetation is made up of species in complete equilibrium both with the general environment and with the microenvironment that determines the success or failure of reproduction. This series of vegetational changes on a single site is called plant or vegetational *succession*. The early changes can be relatively rapid, but eventual stabilization of the vegetation may take centuries.

Any area devoid of plants is bombarded with many seeds and fruits. The area may be a sand bar in a river, polished granite emerging from 10,000 years under a glacier, or it can be a pond newly created by the damming of a creek. All such open areas are subject to invasion by vegetation, but not all succumb easily or at the same rate, and not all seeds or seedlings do well in such open types of environment. The glacially carved rock of the Grand Teton in Wyoming will be quite bare for thousands of years because of its hardness and steepness, the cold environment, and the small number of plants hardy enough to exist there. A pond in Alabama, on the other hand, may fill in with aquatic plants and sediment in only a few years, and in a (relatively) few decades be covered with bottomland forest.

Succession on new areas is called *primary succession*. Such succession must, perforce, always be accompanied by the development of a soil. Vegetational succession and soil development go hand in hand—slowly at first, then more rapidly, and then slowly again—but they cannot be separated nor can one reach stability without the other.

Primary succession starting on bare rock is particularly slow. No matter what the climate, there is no drier microenvironment than that of a rock surface from which water escapes by runoff and by evaporation. The first plants here are likely to be crustose, intricately patterned lichens. These lichens, however, contribute very little to the breakdown of the rock into an elementary soil. The big contributions to vegetational establishment and soil initiation are usually made by moss mats or by herbaceous vascular plants, which get started along deep cracks in the rock. Since these cracks vary in abundance with the type of rock, the speed of succession and soil formation depend to some extent on these rock characteristics.

Succession starting in open water is relatively fast. The northern part of the American Midwest is dotted with forested bogs that were open-water glacial lakes less than 10,000 years ago. Conversely, the bare, glacially polished rocks of the Canadian Shield not far to the north still have little soil or vegetational development.

The first plants to invade a new body of open water are algae, soon followed by submerged aquatic vascular plants such as *Elodea* (*Anacharis*), *Myriophyllum,* and *Potamogeton.* Organic remains and inorganic sediment gradually cause the pond to become shallower. The invasion of emergent aquatic vascular plants such as cattail (*Typha*), bulrush (*Scirpus*), and sedges (*Carex*) speeds up the filling process. Sometimes peat moss (*Sphagnum*) forms a mat over the water surface in shallower places and rapidly contributes its peat to the sediments. Several species of sedges often do the same thing. In cooler climates where organic matter is not readily decomposed, the lake or pond eventually becomes a bog filled primarily with organic matter called *peat* and covered with a characteristic vegetation.

Soil developed in primary succession from open water is made up of a mixture of organic peat and inorganic sediments. The relative amounts of each depend upon the climate and upon the erosion of the pond's watershed. A farm pond on the Carolina Piedmont will fill in with considerable silt and clay and very little peat, but a pond on the Carolina Coastal Plain will slowly fill with peat. The difference lies in the hilly, cultivated, clay land of the Piedmont as contrasted with the flat, sandy, wild lands of the Coastal Plain.

Once a soil has developed, the vegetation over it may be destroyed by fire, grazing, or cultivation. If the soil is not destroyed by erosion caused by the removal of the original vegetation, it provides a ready-made substratum for revegetation. The revegetation is called *secondary succession.* Because it does not need to wait for soil development, it is relatively rapid. Stability is reached in terms of a few centuries as compared to the thousands or tens of thousands of years involved in most primary succession. The abandoned garden and its weeds are stages in secondary succession.

Few regions on earth provide as good an example of secondary succession as does the North Carolina Piedmont. Here, because of a combination of abundant rainfall, moderate temperatures, and the contrasting vegetational types involved, the course of revegetation on abandoned farm land is just enough spread out over the years so that it can be seen and studied easily. On abandoned land in the tropics, however, such succession is often so fast and unruly that it produces a jungle that can be deciphered only by an expert tropical ecologist. In deserts and tundras, succession is often so very slow as to be unnoticed, or the revegetation may be merely a less dense variant of the original vegetation.

The original vegetation of the Piedmont was a forest consisting mostly of deciduous trees such as oaks and hickories, with here and there a loblolly pine or a shortleaf pine. This forest, as contrasted to those of the Coastal Plain, was not easily burned, and so was essentially undisturbed when European settlers arrived early in the eighteenth century. There still are some relatively undisturbed patches of this kind of forest on rocky ground unsuited to cultivation; so we know fairly well what it was like. The land was cleared and crops of tobacco, corn, and cotton were planted on small fields. Since fertilizers were not abundant nor easily available, these nitrogen-using crops exhausted the nitrate supply in the soil. It was necessary to abandon the land, cut down more forest, and plant new fields—a practice that was already being done by the time of the American Revolution and, unfortunately, continued up until the 1930s. The availability of fertilizers and the changes in crops toward permanent pastures or timberland have just about stopped such land abandonment today.

In this example of secondary succession, revegetation starts as soon as cultivation is stopped, even before the crop is harvested. The weeds that invade during the late summer and autumn are primarily crabgrass (*Digitaria sanguinalis*) and horseweed (*Erigeron canadensis*). The horseweed overwinters as a dwarf vegetative rosette, grows up, becomes dominant, and flowers in the first summer after abandonment. During this summer, the horseweed in turn is invaded by small plants of white aster (*Aster pilosus*), which grow up, become dominant, and flower in the second summer, suppressing the horseweed. By the third summer, broomsedge (*Andropogon virginicus*), a tall bunchgrass, has begun to appear and begins to dispossess the aster.

At any of these stages, but particularly at the broomsedge stage, young pine seedlings appear. They grow slowly the first year but in the following years grow rapidly and soon form a complete crown canopy, shading the environment and making it completely unsuitable for the old field plants. This usually occurs between 5 and 10 years after abandonment. The pines continue to grow rapidly; competition between pine individuals becomes intense and many die. The typical scanty herbaceous flora of a pine woods appears on the forest floor. As long as the forest is dominated by pines, there is little or no pine reproduction. Pine seedlings need almost full sunlight for success, and the shade of the dominant pines causes the few pine seedlings to be weak and spindly. There is competition not only for light but also for water. The overstory pines have their roots concentrated in the upper 2 decimeters of soil, where the roots of the pine seedlings are also confined. One has only to cut the roots of the dominant pines by trenching with a spade around a small plot, and refilling the trench, to see what an explosive effect there is on the growth of seedlings when competition for water is removed.

Seedlings of sweet gum (*Liquidambar*) and various oak species are more tolerant of shade than are the pine seedlings. Also, these broad-leaved seedlings have deeper root systems and can tap deeper supplies of soil moisture. Soon a wave of sweet-gum saplings comes up under the pines, then a wave of oak saplings, and later a wave of hickory saplings. All of these saplings are potential overstory trees and grow steadily upward as the pines approach maturity 80–140 years after abandonment. All the while, a layer of true secondary trees is developing: dogwoods, sourwood (*Oxydendrum*), and red maple (*Acer rubrum*). One by one, the old pines die off and are replaced by the deciduous hardwoods, particularly oaks and hickories. After 200 years or so, the forest consists predominantly of deciduous trees and, although minor changes in composition may take place later, succession is essentially over and a forest somewhat resembling the original forest has become established.

Another good place to observe secondary succession is in the sub-alpine zone of the Rocky Mountains where the original vegetation, spruce-fir forest, has been destroyed by fire. Pure stands of lodgepole pine (*Pinus contorta*) come in on these burned areas. Within a century or so, young spruces and firs become established under the pines, and eventually replace them as the older pines die.

In any climate where vegetation is protected from man, disease, insects, or fire, a kind of vegetation will eventually appear in which the seedlings are of the same species as the dominants. This vegetation is in equilibrium with the climate, the soil, and the herbivorous animals. As long as these environmental elements do not change, the vegetation will continue through time with essentially the same species pattern. This vegetation is in dynamic equilibrium with its environment; entrance of other species is almost impossible because of limiting factors, and the vegetation's own growth is kept in check by limiting factors. The vegetation is now in "climax" condition.

*Climax vegetation* is determined by the whole environment—climate, soils, animals, fire, man—acting upon the available regional flora. It is theoretically possible for an entire climatic region to be covered with a single type of climax vegetation. However, because of variations in local environments, particularly in soil parent materials, such a region is more likely to have several or many climax vegetation types. In reality, such a region will be a mosaic of both successional and climax types, as can be seen by traversing it on the ground or by observing it in aerial photographs.

## BALANCE IN THE ECOSYSTEM

Theoretically, it is possible for an ecosystem to attain a *steady-state condition*—that is, the composition and cycling of energy and materials remain essentially the same for a long and indefinite period. Actually, very few ecosystems ever reach this condition. Some reach it for short periods of time but, because of both normal cycles and unpredictable changes in the environment, limiting factors necessary to the maintenance of the steady-state condition may be removed or changed in intensity. The removal of the limiting factor may trigger long chain reactions in the ecosystem because it no longer is in the steady state. Production may increase greatly over consumption, or an increase in herbivores may weaken the producing vegetation and throw the whole system in reverse.

Whether or not it is desirable to maintain steady-state conditions in all terrestrial ecosystems (and there are practical reasons why in certain cases we should not), we should be aware that an ecosystem is a delicate thing under the control of certain limiting factors and that it is headed in a predictable direction because of these factors. Remove one of these limiting factors, such as the coyote on herbivore populations of the grasslands, or introduce an exotic factor such as the chestnut blight disease, and the ecological balance of the system may be destroyed. A series of unpredictable changes may be set up with an end no one can foresee. Any ecosystemic change, natural or man-made, must be viewed with caution.

# 7

# TERRESTRIAL
# ECOSYSTEM
# TYPES

Many kinds of ecosystems have developed on earth from the great number of possible combinations of climate, parent rock, and available flora and fauna (the "biota"). Some of these ecosystems are aquatic, some are terrestrial. In this chapter we will attempt an introduction to the general ecological characteristics of a few of the principal kinds of terrestrial ecosystems.

The types of ecosystems discussed, their locations, and general environmental conditions are listed in Table 7-1, on pp. 98–101. Each of these types is a rather broad category with considerable variation from place to place around the earth. They represent some of the main classes of terrestrial ecosystems.

## TROPICAL RAIN FOREST

Magnificent tropical rain forests (see Fig. 7-1) occur where there is always plenty of moisture and heat, no drought, and no winter. As a result, these forests have a rich floristic and faunistic composition. Plants and animals of all kinds, which have no resistance to drought or cold, occur here. These forests are best developed in tropical America, particularly the Amazon basin, in the East Indies and surrounding areas, and to a lesser extent in Africa.

The typical rain forest has many layers. Dominant trees are generally 80–125 feet high, but there are usually some emergent trees that extend high above the dominant canopy to perhaps 200 feet. Below the crowns of the dominant trees are several other strata of plants that can tolerate deep shade.

A remarkable feature of the rain forest is the concentration of so much life in the canopy, where there is plenty of light. Since there is enough heat and moisture, the principal limiting factor in the rain forest is usually light. The crowns of the large trees are covered

**Fig. 7-1.** *Characteristic buttressing at base of a dominant tree* (Sloanea woollsii, *"carabeen"*) *in a subtropical rain forest in Queensland, Australia. Lianas and flying roots of the strangling fig are visible on the trunk.*

with epiphytes, nonparasitic plants that use the trees only for support. These epiphytic plants manufacture their own food and, with aerial roots or water catchments, get their water from the torrential rains that occur almost daily. In the American rain forest, orchids and bromeliads (relatives of the pineapple) are the most abundant epiphytes. In the East Indies, there are no bromeliads but orchids and ferns are abundant as epiphytes. Lianas, which are vines rooted in the ground but having their leaves and flowers in the canopy a hundred feet above, are also characteristic of all tropical rain forests.

The floristic richness of the rain forest is greater than that of any other ecosystem type; there are thousands of species of orchids alone. The number of tree species is so great that only in a few places do we find rain forests dominated by one or two species. In some places in the Brazilian forests, there are as many as 300 species of trees occurring in a square mile. The field identification of many of these trees is difficult since their crowns are lost in the tangle of the canopy. Also, many species have smooth bark and buttressed bases that look alike. Even the leaves tend to be similar: entire margins, elliptic shape, a "drip" tip off which the water flows easily from the smooth glossy evergreen surface. Of course, there are also many

**Table 7-1.** *Locations and general environmental conditions for certain types of terrestrial ecosystems.*

| Climax Ecosystem Type | Principal Locations | Precipitation Range (inches/year) | Temperature Range (°F) (Daily Maximum and Minimum) | Soils |
|---|---|---|---|---|
| Tropical Rain Forest | Central America (Atlantic coast) Amazon Basin Brazilian coast West African coast Congo Basin Malaya East Indies Philippines New Guinea N.E. Australia Pacific islands | 50–500 Equatorial type: frequent torrential thunderstorms<br><br>Tradewind type: steady, almost daily rains<br><br>No dry period | Little annual variation<br><br>Max.    85–95<br><br>Min.    65–80<br><br>No cold period | Mainly reddish laterites |
| Tropical Savanna | Central America (Pacific coast) Orinoco Basin Brazil, S. of Amazon Basin N. Central Africa East Africa S. Central Africa Madagascar India S.E. Asia Northern Australia | 10–75 Warm season thunderstorms<br><br>Almost no rain in cool season<br><br>Long dry period during low sun | Considerable annual variation; no really cold period<br>*Rainy season (high sun)*<br>Max.    75–90<br>Min.    65–80<br>*Dry season (low sun)*<br>Max.    70–90<br>Min.    55–65<br>*Dry season (higher sun)*<br>Max.    85–105<br>Min.    70–80 | Some laterites; considerable variety |

| | Location | Precipitation (inches) | Temperature (°F) | | Soils |
|---|---|---|---|---|---|
| Broad-Sclerophyll Vegetation | Mediterranean region<br>California<br>Cape of Good Hope region<br>Central Chile<br>S.W. Australia | 10–35<br>Almost all rainfall in cool season<br>Summer very dry | *Winter*<br>Max.<br>Min.<br>*Summer*<br>Max.<br>Min. | 50–75<br>35–50<br><br>65–105<br>55–80 | Terra rossa, noncalcic red soils; considerable variation |
| Temperate Grasslands | Central North America<br>Eastern Europe<br>Central & Western Asia<br>Argentina<br>New Zealand | 12–80<br>Evenly distributed through the year or with a peak in summer<br>Snow in winter | *Winter*<br>Max.<br>Min.<br>*Summer*<br>Max.<br>Min. | 0–65<br>–50–50<br><br>70–120<br>30–60 | Black prairie soils<br>Chernozems<br>Chestnut and brown soils<br>Almost all have a lime layer |
| Warm Deserts | S.W. North America<br>Peru & N. Chile<br>North Africa<br>Arabia<br>S.W. Asia<br>East Africa<br>S.W. Africa<br>Central Australia | 0–10<br>Great irregularity<br>Long dry season, up to several years in most severe deserts | Great diurnal variation<br>Max.<br>Min.<br><br>Frosts rare | 80–135<br>35–75 | Reddish desert soils, often sandy or rocky<br>Some saline soils |
| Cold Deserts | Intermountain W. North America<br>Patagonia<br>Transcaspian Asia<br>Central Asia | 2–8<br>Great irregularity<br>Long dry season<br>Most precip. in winter; some snow | Great diurnal variation<br>*Winter*<br>Max.<br>Min.<br>Frosts common ½–¾ of year<br>*Summer*<br>Max.<br>Min. | 20–60<br>–40–25<br><br>75–110<br>40–70 | Gray desert soils, often sandy or rocky<br>Some saline soils |

**Table 7-1.** (*Continued*)

| Climax Ecosystem Type | Principal Locations | Precipitation Range (inches/year) | Temperature Range (°F) (Daily Maximum and Minimum) | | Soils |
|---|---|---|---|---|---|
| Temperate Deciduous Forest | Eastern N. America<br>Western Europe<br>Eastern Asia | 25–90<br>Evenly distributed through year<br>Droughts rare<br>Some snow | *Winter*<br>Max.<br>Min.<br>*Summer*<br>Max.<br>Min. | 10–70<br>−20–45<br><br>75–100<br>60–80 | Gray-brown podzolic<br>Red and yellow podzolic |
| Temperate Rain Forest | N.W. Pacific coast, North America<br>W. coast, New Zealand<br>Southern Chile<br>Tasmania & S.E. Australia | 50–350<br>Evenly distributed through year; wetter in winter<br>Some snow | *Winter*<br>Max.<br>Min.<br>*Summer*<br>Max.<br>Min. | 35–50<br>25–45<br><br>55–70<br>50–65 | Podzolic, deep humus |
| Montane Coniferous Forests | Western North America<br>Appalachian N. America<br>European mts.<br>Asian mts. | 15–100<br>Evenly distributed or with summer dry season<br>Snow may be very deep in winter | *Winter*<br>Max.<br>Min.<br>*Summer*<br>Max.<br>Min. | −20–60<br>−55–35<br><br>45–80<br>20–60 | Various, podzolic, often shallow, rocky |

100

| | | | Temperature | | |
|---|---|---|---|---|---|
| Boreal Coniferous Forest | Northern N. America<br>Northern Europe<br>Northern Asia | 15–40<br>Evenly distributed<br>Much snow | *Winter* Max. −35–30<br>Min. −65–15<br>*Summer* Max. 50–70<br>Min. 20–55 | | True podzols<br>Bog soils<br>Some permafrost at depth, in places |
| Alpine Tundras | Western N. America<br>N. Appalachian N. America<br>European mts.<br>Asian mts.<br>Andes<br>African volcanoes<br>New Zealand | 30–80<br>Much winter snow; long-persisting snowbanks | *Winter* Max. −35–30<br>Min. −60–10<br>*Summer* Max. 40–70<br>Min. 15–35 | | Usually rocky<br>Some turf and bog soils<br>Polygons and stone nets<br>Some permafrost |
| Arctic Tundra | Northern N. America<br>Greenland<br>Northern Eurasia | 10–30<br>Considerable snow | *Winter* Max. −40–20<br>Min. −70– 0<br>*Summer* Max. 35–60<br>Min. 30–45 | | Rocky or boggy<br>Much patterned ground<br>Permafrost |

other kinds of leaf forms in this forest, as might be expected with the diversity of families represented.

The animal life dependent on this highly productive vegetation is also quite varied. All trophic levels are represented in abundance. Many of the animals live only in the canopy where so much of the production originates: monkeys, lemurs, snakes, birds, insects. The canopy biota of the rain forest is an amazing collection of an almost infinite variety of adaptations to special ecological niches, and an unsurpassed (but exceedingly complex) place for the study of the evolution of ecological relationships.

As an ecosytem, the tropical rain forest is the most productive of all. Almost no figures are available on rain-forest productivity, but it seems safe to say that the net productivity of above-ground plant parts is in the range of 10 to 20 grams/meter$^2$/day throughout most of the year. Much of this, of course, goes into wood, which supports eventually only organisms such as termites, fungi, and bacteria. As might be expected, the weight and activity of decomposers are very great.

Although the principal limiting factor is usually light, with so great a weight of organisms per unit area, probably at any particular time much of the mineral reservoir is tied up in the standing crop. This could mean that, locally, phosphorus, nitrogen, or some other necessary element is limiting.

Man is steadily encroaching on the rain forest: lumbering, clearing for plantations, and other kinds of agriculture. As a result, the rain forest in many places has been eliminated or decimated and replaced by scrub or open savanna, which are subject to annual fires. The undisturbed rain forest maintains its own high humidity and moisture and is difficult to burn, but it can disappear gradually by progressive disturbance around the edges. Small clearings rapidly fill in with the dense growth of tropical secondary succession; however, if the rain forest is once destroyed over a large area, it is almost impossible for it to become re-established.

## TROPICAL SAVANNA

Tropical savanna (see Fig. 7-2) is grassland often dotted here and there with trees or with patches of open forest. Some savannas are quite arid, with only scattered thorny trees; others have almost complete tree cover.

Most tropical savanna is climatically caused, but some undoubtedly results from the opening up and destruction of rain forest. True

**Fig. 7-2.** *Subtropical savanna of "ironbarks"* (Eucalyptus mel-anophloea *and* E. crebra) *and grass* (Themeda australis) *in Queensland, Australia. Summer rainfall type.*

savanna climate is characterized by warmth the year round but with a dry season during the period of low sun; this is also the "cool" season but just before rains come in "summer" the weather becomes very hot. So there are really three seasons in the savanna: warm and rainy, cool and dry, and hot and dry.

Savanna exists in South America and Africa north and south of the equatorial rain forest. Much of southern Asia, particularly India, is savanna.

The vegetation of most savannas is dominated by tall grasses, which become dry and often burn during the dry season. Scattered throughout the grassland are relatively low, often flat-topped, thorny trees, which may be deciduous or evergreen. Many of the trees are members of the legume family. There are so many kinds of savannas in so many widely scattered places that it is not possible here to characterize them floristically. Like all tropical vegetations, the flora is usually rich but there is a tendency for grasses and legumes to be well represented.

Because of the high production of grasses and the open nature of the vegetation, tropical savannas in their original conditions often have great numbers of hooved grazing mammals. Preying on these are large carnivores, such as the lion in Africa and the tiger in Asia.

The productivity of tropical savannas is probably less than that of most tropical rain forests, but much more of the productivity probably goes into readily digestible food for large animals. The result is the abundance of such animals and their predators. The principal limiting factor, of course, is water, which limits growth to usually no more than half the year.

Man has had a tremendous impact on the savannas through fire, agriculture, and hunting. As a result, even though because of fire there is more savanna land than there used to be, most of it is fairly well disturbed. The great herds of wild animals are disappearing rapidly except in such places as the Kreuger National Park in South Africa.

## BROAD-SCLEROPHYLL VEGETATION

This ecosystem type is dominated by scrubby, woody plants, many of which have a broad, hard, evergreen leaf. However, underneath and scattered among these sclerophyllous trees and shrubs are numerous grasses and herbaceous flowering plants.

**Fig. 7-3.** *Broad-sclerophyll vegetation of evergreen and deciduous oaks and grass, foothills of Sierra Nevada, California. Winter rainfall type.*

Broad-sclerophyll vegetation (see Fig. 7-3) is characteristic of what is called the "Mediterranean" climate, which has mild, damp winters but hot, dry summers with blue skies and seldom a drop of rain. In the Mediterranean region itself—southern France, Spain, Portugal,

North Africa, Israel, Lebanon, Turkey, Greece, and Italy—the scrubby vegetation is known as *maquis* (or *macchia* or *garigue*). In California, it is *chaparral* where dense and scrubby, and *live oak woodland* where open and dominated by trees and grass. There are also well-developed examples of broad-sclerophyll vegetation in the Southern Hemisphere, particularly in southwestern Australia, in the Cape of Good Hope region in South Africa, and in central Chile.

The vegetation varies from dense, almost impenetrable, spiny scrub to open, grassy woodlands. In the Mediterranean region, the woodlands have almost disappeared because of the effects of 3,000 years of civilization, and have been replaced by olive groves, vineyards, or, in the rockier places, by the native scrub (maquis and garigue). The trees and shrubs are evergreen with characteristically hard, leathery leaves, which are either small or medium size. The herbaceous plants are green and flowering during the winter and spring rainy period but become yellow, dry, and susceptible to fire in the very dry summers. The flowers of these herbaceous plants are often showy and fragrant.

Since the broad-sclerophyll regions are so isolated from each other, their vegetations probably originated from quite different floristic stocks; this appears to be particularly so in the Southern Hemisphere. California and the Mediterranean areas have a little more in common with oaks, pines, and some other genera occurring widely in both. However, each of these has its own many endemic species. While both the "Mediterranean" climate and the physiognomy of the broad-sclerophyll vegetation are similar in all five locations, the floras of the regions are quite distinct. In fact, the Cape of Good Hope region has one of the most distinctive of all continental floras, with 2,600 species in the very small area of 200 square miles. A high proportion of these are endemic to that region. Many species native to the Cape region grow as introduced ornamentals in California, which is climatically similar. Examples are some of the geraniums (*Pelargonium*), Gerber daisy, ice plant, and many heathers.

The broad-sclerophyll ecosystem is not highly productive because of the long dry season. Therefore, its animal life is not particularly abundant. In California, however, it was well developed until the middle of the nineteenth century; herbivores such as ground squirrels, deer, and elk, and carnivores such as the mountain lion and California grizzly bear were common. In southwestern Australia, kangaroos and other marsupials evolved and filled similar ecological niches in the sclerophyll ecosystem.

Man has found this climatic type particularly to his liking for both specialized agriculture and personal living. The result has been great inroads on the native vegetation and animal life by cultivation, hunting, and fire, and now by cities and highway systems.

## TEMPERATE GRASSLANDS

Most areas of the great temperate grasslands (see Fig. 7-4) are now occupied by cultivated grasses such as wheat and corn or are under controlled grazing. However, until the late nineteenth century, they were still covered by their original vegetation and occupied by large herds of bison and other hooved mammals. The best examples of these

**Fig. 7-4.** *Temperate grassland on the high plains of western Nebraska. Principal grasses pictured are blue grama* (Bouteloua gracilis) *and false buffalo grass* (Munroa squarrosa). *Pricklypear cactus* (Opuntia polyacantha) *is also present. Cottonwoods* (Populus sargentii) *mark the course of the South Platte River in the distance.*

grasslands are the North American prairies and plains, the Eurasian steppes, the Argentine pampas, and the tussock grasslands of New Zealand.

The vegetation is dominated by grasses, legumes, and composites but with many other families represented so that there is great floristic diversity. In regions with relatively high precipitation, the original grasses often stand over 6 feet high, with legumes and composites to match. In the drier parts, there is only a patchy sod a few inches high.

The principal limiting factors to the invasion of the moister grasslands by trees are fire and the occurrence of series of drought years. The American prairie seems to be enhanced by fire, since protection from fire brings invasion by various species of trees. But in the drier plains there can be no tree invasion. A combination of fire and occasional drought allowed the prairie to exist in many places where the climate could, and now does, support trees.

Man has converted the temperate grasslands to his own agricultural use only in the last century or two—the American prairie and the Hungarian *puszta* after the middle of the nineteenth century, and the steppes of Central Asia only in this century. The fertile prairie soils and chernozems of Illinois, Iowa, and Nebraska have made these agricultural regions as productive as any in the world. However, the annual net productivity of original prairie vegetation is only about 0.5 to 2 grams dry weight of shoots per square meter per day. On an annual basis, a crop of corn (maize) on prairie land will produce above-ground vegetation at the rate of 2.5 to 3 grams of dry weight per square meter per day. However, it does this in a growing season of only 125 to 150 days so that productivity figures based on the growing season alone are about 7.5 grams dry weight per square meter per day, a productivity considerably higher than that of the native vegetation (Ovington et al., 1963).

In North America the original prairie ecosystem was dominated by many kinds of grasses and legumes which formed the basis of a food chain that ran from the bison, pronghorn antelope, and elk, to the wolf, coyote, panther, and man. The plains Indians were members of trophic level 3 $(T_3)$ and subsisted largely on the buffalo and other game and to a lesser extent on roots, fruits, and seeds. When professional buffalo-hide hunters killed off the bison in the 1870s and farmers and ranchers appeared, the old ecosystem was gone forever. The Indians had to join the new controlled ecosystem or perish.

## DESERTS

Desert ecosystems occupy climates too dry for grasslands. The vegetation (see Fig. 7-5) consists of widely scattered thorny bushes, perhaps a few succulents such as cacti or Euphorbias, and, after rains, usually some, small, ephemeral annual plants. Most deserts receive some rain every year, but where rain falls only once in several years, as on the northern coast of Chile, the ground may appear absolutely

**Fig. 7-5.** *Cold-desert vegetation in Nevada. Shadscale* (Atriplex confertifolia) *is the principal shrub in the picture. Note the well-marked desert pavement of pebbles.*

barren. After the rare rains, however, there is a light green covering of annuals, which come up quickly from long-lived, buried seeds.

Deserts may be classified roughly as being either warm deserts or cold deserts. The warm deserts are tropical and subtropical with no winter or a very mild one. The vegetation of warm deserts consists mainly of plants from tropical families and genera. Cold deserts may have severe winters; their vegetation has been derived principally from the Tertiary mountain flora and, to some extent, from the flora of saline marshes and dunes along the colder seacoasts. The two kinds of deserts have one thing in common: lack of water through most of the year.

Desert ecosystems differ from each other floristically, particularly so in the tropics. The cold deserts of western Asia and those of western North America do have many genera in common and also have similar climates. Life forms and productivity in the two are much alike. In warm deserts, which apparently have originated somewhat independently of each other, there has been parallel evolution to fill every ecological niche. Plants may look alike in different warm deserts but often are not closely related. For example, the large branched cacti in North American warm deserts resemble the large branched Euphorbias in African deserts.

Productivity in all desert ecosystems is low owing to the limiting factor of drought. Cold deserts also have low temperature as a limiting factor during a great part of the year. Growth is thus limited to a short period between winter cold and summer drought. Even during this relatively favorable period, productivity is usually somewhat less than 0.5 gram of dry matter per square meter per day. Much of this small production goes into woody tissue. This is in contrast to the production of digestible foods in grasslands. Consequently, although there is an interesting and diverse animal life in deserts, the weight in animals per unit area is not very large.

Compared to other ecosystems, desert ecosystems, except for oases and irrigated lands, have been relatively unchanged by man. However, the need for more arable land and the development of modern irrigation methods are continually bringing more desert land into agriculture. Diversion of distant water supplies and the development of air conditioning have allowed extensive spread of cities in the deserts of the southwestern United States.

## TEMPERATE DECIDUOUS FOREST

As was stated in earlier chapters, much of the old Arcto-Tertiary forest was winter deciduous. Several million years ago, this forest extended throughout the Northern Hemisphere. The glacial ice and droughts of the Pleistocene cut it into three main parts: western Europe, eastern Asia, and eastern North America. As a result of severe glaciation, the western European segment is somewhat poorer floristically than the other two.

With the rise of western civilization and the expansion of population in Europe, most of the original forests were cleared for fuel and lumber, and the land became occupied by crops. Before the forests completely disappeared, the development of forestry as an applied science put the remaining forests under such rigorous management that very little untamed deciduous forest exists in Europe. The same thing happened to the forests of eastern Asia; forestry arrived there later and after great loss of forest area.

The most magnificent deciduous forests of all were in eastern North America. These forests lasted longer because the American Indian inhabitants were relatively few in number. Also, the Indians depended upon the forest ecosystem for their livelihood—that is, for hunting and for gathering wild fruits, seeds, and roots. Their garden plots were rather small and required little forest area. When Europeans arrived on the scene, the forests were soon converted into agricultural land. The forests were saved from completely disappearing, however, by the vast American prairie to the west, which provided enough agricultural land to supply all of America. Many farms in the forested area were

**Fig. 7-6.** *Temperate deciduous forest of tulip tree* (Liriodendron tulipifera), *sugar maple* (Acer saccharum), *yellow buckeye* (Aesculus octandra), *and several other species on Kimsey Creek in the southern Appalachian Mountains of North Carolina. Photograph courtesy of U.S. Forest Service.*

abandoned and have since been covered by successional forest. Some excellent, though small, areas of original deciduous forest have also been preserved in national and state parks, in national forests, and in private holdings. The best examples are in the Great Smoky Mountains National Park and national forests of western North Carolina and eastern Tennessee. From these scattered remnants we can get some idea of what the original, almost unbroken, forest was like. (See Fig.7-6.)

Essentially, the deciduous forest has five layers:

1. An overstory of deciduous trees with crown tops 75–175 feet above the ground.
2. A secondary deciduous tree stratum with tops 20–35 feet.
3. A shrub layer, deciduous and evergreen, 1–8 feet.
4. A herbaceous layer, largely of spring perennials, with rhizomes and bulbs.
5. A moss and lichen layer, developed primarily on fallen logs and rocks.

In eastern North America, the most luxuriant deciduous forests are the cove hardwood forests of the southern Appalachians. These are remnants of the Tertiary forests, and thus are floristically diverse. There are many kinds of dominant trees: buckeyes (*Aesculus*), basswoods (*Tilia*), beech (*Fagus*), tulip trees (*Liriodendron*), hemlock (*Tsuga*), silver bells (*Halesia*), and many others. To the north, in the Lake States and New England, beech and maple (*Acer*) tend to dominate the deciduous forest, while to the east, south, and west, in a great horseshoe around the south end of the Appalachians, oaks (*Quercus*) and hickories (*Carya*) are the dominants.

The original animal life was abundant with deer, bear, panthers, squirrels, and wild turkeys. Large animals became scarce during the peak of agricultural use, but populations have increased with the return of the forest environment and scientific restocking of game.

The deciduous forest is fairly productive but not as much so as the tropical rain forest. Ecologists at the University of Minnesota found that oak woodland in Minnesota had a net productivity of 2.5–3.0 grams per meter$^2$ per day on an annual basis, but if calculated only on the growing season the productivity is about 6 grams per meter$^2$ per day. Productivity is probably higher than this in the more diverse deciduous forests farther south. Conifer forests successional to deciduous forests in the southeastern United States are probably even more highly productive since they are not in a steady-state condition.

Limiting factors vary from place to place, but generally low temperature is limiting in the north, aridity toward the west, and lack or excess of certain minerals limit growth on certain soil types.

## TEMPERATE RAIN FOREST

The long strip of rain forest along the northwestern Pacific Coast of North America is a fine example of wet temperate forest. Cool climate rain forests such as this occur only in a few places besides northwestern North America: southern Chile, the west coasts of New Zealand (see Fig. 7-7), and Tasmania and southeastern Australia. The latitudes are usually about 40–55 degrees, where the stormy westerly winds bring in deep cyclonic storms from the ocean. Where these storms cross the coastal mountains, the result is heavy rainfall, especially in winter. On the Olympic Peninsula in Washington, precipitation averages as high as 140 inches per year; on the southwest coast of the South Island of New Zealand it is even higher—up to 350 inches per year. The result is an abundance of water, and, because of

**Fig. 7-7.** *Temperate evergreen rain forest of rimu* (Dacrydium cupressinum), *kahikatea* (Podocarpus dacrydioides), *and rata* (Metrosideros lucida) *on the west coast of South Island, New Zealand. Epiphytic bryophytes and ferns are abundant. The long-leaved climbing vine is* Freycinetia banksii *of the Pandanus family.*

the cool climate, the evapotranspiration rate is relatively low so that the forest is literally dripping for much of the year.

The rain forests in North America are dominated almost completely by very large coniferous trees: in the south, redwood (*Sequoia sempervirens*), which reaches heights of well over 300 feet; in the north, Douglas fir (*Pseudotsuga menziesii*), giant arbor-vitae (*Thuja plicata*), Sitka spruce (*Picea sitchensis*), and western hemlock (*Tsuga heterophylla*). In the Southern Hemisphere, the New Zealand rain forests are dominated also mainly by conifers but of the family Podocarpaceae: rimu (*Dacrydium cupressinum*), kahikatea (*Podocarpus dacrydioides*), and several others. In addition to the podocarps, there are several kinds of tree ferns and many dicotyledonous trees, particularly the evergreen Southern Hemisphere beeches belonging to the genus *Nothofagus*. This same genus, along with podocarps, is found in both the Chilean and Australian temperate rain forests.

The trees of temperate rain forests, including the dicots, are almost entirely evergreen except for some of the Chilean species of *Nothofagus* and North American maples and alders, which are deciduous.

The trees are festooned with pendants of mosses, liverworts, and filmy ferns. As the epiphytic orchids and bromeliads typify the tropical rain forests, so these epiphytic bryophytes and miniature ferns typify the temperate rain forests. They cover everything from living branches and leaves to rotting logs, and help to give the forest its characteristic green, fresh look, particularly in the rain when they drip with water.

Because of the cool climate, decomposers work slowly; log piles upon log to form a moss and fern-covered jumble over the forest floor, which is deep in humus. This is very unlike the tropical rain forest, where decomposers make short work of the dead leaves and trunks so that the forest floor has little humus and few fallen logs at any given time.

Productivity is fairly high in these forests but it chiefly goes into wood. Available forage is not high, so that the biomass of large animals is not great, although deer, elk, and mountain lions form parts of the American rain-forest ecosystem. In New Zealand, no mammals or reptiles existed in the original forest. The ecological niches were filled by birds: ground-foraging ones such as the kiwi (*Apterix*), weka (*Gallirallus*), and takahe (*Nothornis*), kakapos which are tree-climbing, flightless parrots (*Strigops*), and carnivorous parrots such as the kea (*Nestor*).

The principal limiting factor to productivity in the temperate rain forest is probably the low mean annual temperature. Another may be the lack of certain minerals. The distributional limits of the ecosystem are determined by heavy rainfall and low evaporation; drought cannot be tolerated for long.

Man's effect has been principally through timber cutting and resultant fires. In spite of the high rainfall, periods of drought up to two or three weeks can occur, and the forest with its resinous foliage and dry mosses becomes a tinder box. Many areas in the northwestern United States have been heavily deforested and burned. Parts of the beautiful forest on the west coast of New Zealand have shared the same fate. Fortunately, national parks in both countries have preserved large areas in their original condition, and modern "sustained yield" forestry promises to use the producing forests wisely.

In New Zealand, the introduction of many species of deer proved to be a serious mistake, since the forests had evolved in the absence of grazing mammals. Elk, moose, European red deer, mule deer, and many other species have seriously overbrowsed these forests. The forest ecosystem has been thrown out of balance by great population increases of deer, since the ecosystem has relatively high productivity but low recuperative powers.

## MONTANE CONIFEROUS FORESTS

There seems to be an affinity between mountains and forests. Except in the polar and extreme desert regions, wherever there are mountains the slopes are usually covered with woodlands or forests (see Fig. 7-8). This situation is due both to the effect of the mountain mass in inducing precipitation as either rain or snow, and also to the presence of rock on or near the surface. Surprisingly enough, many kinds of trees thrive better in this rocky substratum than in the deep allu-

**Fig. 7-8.** *Open montane evergreen forest of* Pinus jeffreyi *typical of early day western yellow pine forests where ground fires kept undergrowth down. East slope of Sierra Nevada, California. Ground is snow covered.*

vium of the valleys. This is particularly true in the mountains of dry regions, where forests usually avoid the alluvial valleys and the trees may cling to rocky cliffs.

Since high mountains extend vertically through several climatic zones, their vegetation is usually rather sharply marked off into zones. In the Northern Hemisphere, these vegetational zones usually are dominated by different kinds of cone-bearing trees, such as pines, firs, spruces, junipers, and hemlocks. Only in the Appalachian Mountains and the eastern Asian mountains do deciduous forests occupy great areas of mountainside. Temperate mountain areas are relatively small in the Southern Hemisphere. The flora of each particular area is rather distinct, so that one cannot generalize concerning the nature of these southern montane forests. But in the three continents of the Northern Hemisphere, the pines, and their relatives the spruces and firs, dominate the forest zones of most mountain ranges.

The climates of these montane coniferous forests range from hot and relatively dry to cold, wet, and snowy. The nature of the forest vegetation reflects this wide climatic span. The sparse woodlands of pinyon pine and juniper on the desert mountains of southern California and Nevada contrast strongly with the mossy and cool spruce-fir forests of the cloud-shrouded Great Smoky Mountains of North Carolina and Tennessee. On any high mountain range, the usual climatic gradient is from somewhat warm and relatively dry near the base to colder, wetter, and more snowy and windy on the upper slopes. If a mountain is high enough, the climate of the crest may be too severe for forests. In such a place, there will be a more or less marked timberline. Above these scrubby and wind-beaten trees, the truly alpine environment is typified by low plants, rocks, and persistent snowbanks.

The situation on San Francisco Peaks near Flagstaff, Arizona, is a good example of coniferous forest zonation on a high mountain. This isolated mountain, the highest in Arizona, is a dormant volcano rising above the rolling Coconino Plateau to an elevation of 12,670 feet above sea level. Because it is so much higher than the surrounding country, it causes more snow to fall in winter and gets more frequent rain from summer thundershowers. In 1889, the San Francisco Peaks area was chosen by C. Hart Merriam of the U.S. Biological Survey as an ideal mountain on which to study the effects of climate on the distribution of plants and animals. His classic report of 1890 on the results of this investigation stimulated further research on mountain zonation.

Figure 7-9 is a diagram, modified from one in Merriam's report, of the vegetational zones on San Francisco Peaks as viewed from the east side. If we were to start up the mountain from the Painted Desert near the Little Colorado River, at about 4,000 feet above sea level we would be surrounded by the green and maroon cliffs and bare soils of the desert, with only a few scattered bushes and tufts of grass to represent vegetation. As we climbed gradually to the southwest toward the peak, the first trees we would see are the low, rounded, gray-green pinyon pines and bronze-green junipers, which form an open and scrubby woodland starting at about 5,000 feet. This pinyon-juniper

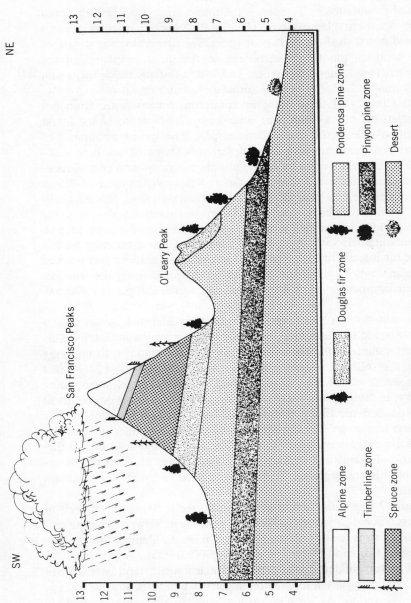

**Fig. 7-9.** *Diagram of vegetational zonation on San Francisco Peaks, Arizona, as viewed from the southeast. From Merriam (1890).*

Alpine zone

Timberline zone

Spruce zone

Douglas fir zone

Ponderosa pine zone

Pinyon pine zone

Desert

San Francisco Peaks

O'Leary Peak

SW

NE

Altitude (in thousands of feet)

116

zone is of variable width, extending up to 6,000 or 7,000 feet depending upon the kind of rock and direction of slope. Near its upper edge, in the draws and ravines where there is more soil moisture, we would begin to see some tall long-needled pines; these are ponderosa pines characteristic of the next zone above. A little farther up, all the north-facing slopes are covered with ponderosa pine forest, while the warmer south-facing slopes still maintain the pinyon woodland. At about 7,000 feet we would come out on the Coconino Plateau at the base of the peak. On this part of the Plateau, the limestones, sandstones, and shales of the Grand Canyon and Painted Desert areas have been covered with lava from the peak and the smaller craters around it. At elevations of 7,000–7,500 feet, the lava plateau is covered with a magnificent open forest of ponderosa pine. This pine forest forms a belt around the mountain and extends upward to about 8,000 feet where it is replaced, first on the north-facing slopes and a little higher on all slopes, by the Douglas fir (*Pseudotsuga*). Aspen is common in this zone; the limber pine occurs on rockier and drier places.

At about 9,000 feet, the Douglas fir zone merges into a zone of Engelmann spruce and corkbark fir. This spruce-fir forest is much like the spruce-fir forest found at much lower elevations farther north (e.g., about 6,000 feet in Glacier National Park, Montana), but the fir there is a different variety. A number of the flowering plants of the forest floor are typical of the trans-Canadian forest of the far north. In the rockier places are limber pines and old bristlecone pines. On the south-facing slopes, this forest extends upward to the timberline at about 11,500 feet, but on the north-facing slopes it dwindles out at about 11,000 feet. Here wind, low temperatures, and snow combine to produce an environment unfavorable to the growth of even these hardy trees. The remainder of the peak extending another 1,000–1,500 feet to the summit at 12,670 feet is a rocky and snowy alpine tundra of low herbaceous plants. Several of the species found in this severe summit environment are characteristic not only of the high peaks of the Rocky Mountains and the Alps but of the arctic regions of northern Alaska and Greenland. From this windswept and barren peak, one can look down over the series of forest zones to the desert stretching eastward to the horizon.

Although other mountain ranges in other parts of the earth show variations in zonation both climatically and biologically, in general the gradients are the same, and the forest zones in many cases are dominated or characterized by cone-bearing trees. Few regions, however, possess as rich a conifer flora amid varied climates as does mountainous western North America. The result is an array of vegetational zonation patterns ranging from the Sierra Nevada of California to the Black Hills of South Dakota.

Since every species of animal prefers a certain kind of environment, mammals, birds, reptiles, and insects are zonally distributed on these high mountains. Pinyon jays may congregate in the dwarf conifers in the lower zones; arctic-alpine birds such as ptarmigans, brown in summer and white in winter, can be seen in the alpine tundra if one looks sharply for them. Every kind of animal, as each plant species, has its own particular altitudinal distribution. However, the nature of each forest belt as determined by the dominant trees often produces sharp boundaries in some of these species distributions. Some species of small rodents prefer the spruce-fir forest, whereas others are better adapted to the open ponderosa pine. On the other hand, many large herbivores such as the elk and mule deer migrate up and down the mountain with the changing seasons.

Maximal primary productivity in these forest zones probably occurs somewhere on the middle slopes of the mountains, although almost no data are available to show this. Productivity probably decreases above that point because of the presence of snow and the cold, short growing season, and decreases below it because of the increasing aridity. In other words, lack of high enough temperatures would limit productivity on the upper part of the mountain, and lack of sufficient water is the limiting factor at the lower elevations.

Modern man has caused many changes in the mountain ecosystems of North America by fire, grazing, lumbering, and recreation activities. The incidence of forest fires has increased even as forest-fire protection services have restricted the once wide-ranging ground fires to relatively small areas. Many subalpine areas in the Rocky Mountains are now occupied by successional lodgepole pine forests, which cover old burned areas in the spruce-fir zone. The desolation caused by catastrophic fires such as the great Tillamook burn of 1933 in the Oregon coastal mountains is astounding. Yet, conversely, protection from the perennial ground fires of the past is changing the nature of many forests. This is particularly true of the ponderosa pine forests of Arizona, which were open and parklike in the nineteenth century. Today, fire protection has helped to produce an understory of dense clumps of young pine trees that prevent the growth of grass. Undoubtedly, this change in the tree-grass balance has resulted in changes in the animal populations also.

Whether the changes made by or because of man in the mountain forests are for better or for worse is not yet known. Some of the effects are easy to see and to predict; others are more subtle and their effects appear only after many years.

## BOREAL CONIFEROUS FOREST

Stretching around the Northern Hemisphere in the subpolar latitudes is a great, almost trackless, coniferous forest of spruces, pines, and firs. The Russians call it the "taiga"; we sometimes call it that, or frequently the "North Woods" or the *boreal forest* (see Fig. 7-10).

**Fig. 7-10.** *Boreal forest or taiga of white spruce* (Picea glauca) *and black spruce* (Picea mariana) *in Alberta, Canada.*

In Eurasia, it extends from Norway across Sweden, Finland, Russia, and Siberia almost to the shores of the Pacific and the Bering Sea. Across the Bering Straits, it reappears in Alaska and sweeps southeastward in a great belt across Canada to Newfoundland. The southern boundaries of this forest are not always sharp, but the northern boundaries form the arctic timberline with the tundra. In North America, the forest extends as far south as northern Minnesota, northern Michigan, and northern New England. Because of its similarity to the subalpine spruce-fir forests of the great mountain systems, its boundaries in the northern Appalachians and Rocky Mountains are not very clear-cut. In eastern North America, the forest extends northward only to Labrador and northern Quebec at about latitude 58 degrees north.

In the west, it extends north of the Arctic Circle almost to the shore of the Arctic Ocean in the lower valley of the Mackenzie River. Great areas of boreal forest also lie north of the Arctic Circle in Siberia.

The climate of the boreal forest is severe. The winters are cold and snowy; the summers are short. The climate is analogous to the climates of the spruce-fir zones of high mountains, but with a little less snow and even lower winter temperatures than in these mountain forests. The fact that the vegetation of the boreal forest and the subalpine forests is similar indicates the similarity of the climates. However, the boreal forest climate has a little less precipitation, is somewhat colder in winter, less windy, and has longer summer days than its mountain counterparts. In its northern parts, trees survive in a climate so severe that it is a wonder that they are there at all. Only a handful of tree species among the thousands on earth have evolved a fitness to the severe environmental selection operating at the northern edge of the boreal forest. Nowhere else in the world are there trees able to grow with so little heat and able to tolerate such low temperatures as these boreal outposts. The only other trees that approach this tolerance are their relatives at timberlines on the high mountains where wind tends to keep timberline lower than temperature itself might allow.

The typical soil of the boreal forest is called a *podzol.* These podzols are covered by a thick layer of dead leaves, twigs, and cones which gradually decays into black humus. The litter and humus layers are thicker than those in warmer forests because bacterial and fungus decomposition of the dead leaves is retarded by low temperatures. This slow, damp decomposition results in the formation of humic acids, which percolate down through the soil with rain water. These acid waters leach out calcium and other bases, and even clays. This leaching leaves the upper part of the mineral soil a layer of ash-white sand. This is the characteristic mark of the true podzol; one cannot fail to recognize it when digging down into such a soil. The true podzol and the boreal forest are almost inseparable. Even the mountain spruce-fir forests seldom have the ash-white horizon. Below the white layer is usually a dark, cemented horizon with clays, humus, and the bases that were leached out of the surface soil. This hardpan layer may prevent good drainage of the soil and also root penetration of the trees.

Because of the relatively recent glaciation there are many lakes in the boreal forest. Since decomposition is slow in the cold climate, these lakes gradually fill in with peat, organic matter produced by sphagnum moss or sedges. The lake may be partially or completely covered with a floating mat of peat with shrubs and trees growing on the rather springy and unstable mat. Eventually, the whole lake becomes a peat bog without open water or perhaps with only a moat around the edges. Since peat is almost entirely organic, these bogs have a somewhat different vegetation from the surrounding podzols. Certain shrubs and herbaceous plants such as sundews and pitcher plants are found there, and nowhere else in the forest. In recent years, such peat has been "mined" and sacked for use in gardens. Its excellent water-storing and water-releasing properties make it valuable in almost any soil from sands to clays.

Peat is also an excellent insulator. In the far north, it keeps summer heat from completely thawing the frozen ground below the depth of a foot or two. This subsoil, called *permafrost,* remains permanently frozen and has probably been this way for thousands of years. Above it in the bog, annual freezing and thawing of the peaty soil pushes against the trees since it cannot push the solid permafrost down. This annual freeze-thaw cycle produces a topsy-turvy "drunken" forest with tree trunks leaning in all directions.

Compared to forests in warmer climates, the boreal forest is simple in structure, both from the standpoint of the few species present and in the way the individual plants are arranged. There usually are about four layers in the forest: an evergreen tree stratum, with the tops of the crowns 40–70 feet above the soil; a shrub stratum 2–4 feet high; a layer of low, scattered herbaceous plants, including ferns; and a very low moss and lichen layer. There are modifications and variations on this theme from place to place but it is surprisingly widespread.

The dominant trees are mostly spruces. Firs and pines are associated with spruce in certain geographic areas. The spruces and firs, in particular, have narrow, cone-shaped crowns with long, tapering tops. In the American boreal forest, the most widespread tree is white spruce (*Picea glauca*), which ranges from Newfoundland and New England to Alaska. In the eastern half of the forest, it is accompanied by balsam fir (*Abies balsamea*). The most common pine is the jack pine (*Pinus banksiana*). The principal broadleaf trees in the forest are canoe birch (*Betula papyrifera*), the peeling white-barked trunks of which are so conspicuous in the north; the balsam poplar (*Populus balsamifera*); and the quaking aspen (*Populus tremuloides*). Extensive stands of aspen usually indicate past destruction of the conifer forest by fire. Other tree species, particularly the black spruce (*Picea mariana*), occur here and there in the forest in specialized environments such as bogs or muskegs. In general, the forest is surprisingly the same across the entire transcontinental span. In Eurasia, the same genera (spruce, fir, pine, poplar, birch) are the taiga dominants; only the species differ, since their evolution has proceeded in the semi-isolation provided by the oceans.

The shrubby and herbaceous plants also show a remarkable sameness in species from place to place. This is also true of the ferns, mosses, and lichens. A northern European and a Canadian would feel prefectly at home in each other's forests.

Typical animals of the boreal forest vary a little more from place to place than do the plants. Yet, in North America, the moose with its diet of willows and water plants and the beaver which feeds on the aspen are as widespread as the forest itself. Numerous kinds of rodents live on the conifer seeds, and the black bear eats blueberries and anything else that is handy. In the north, caribou migrate into the forest annually from the open barrens and tundra to the north.

Little is known of the basic productivity of the taiga except in terms of tree volumes per unit area, as compiled by European and American foresters. Because of low temperatures, productivity is undoubtedly lower than in other forests of moist regions. Its greatest economic value is as a producer of wood for lumber and paper pulp, although the day may come when its recreation value to a crowded world may mean even more. At present, this forest is scarcely utilized for wood except in Europe and only here and there in North America and Asia. In spite of low temperatures, it has great potential for future use because its great area offsets the effects of such temperatures on productivity.

The boreal forest is as yet little affected by man except for fires; it is still a great wilderness, and may remain so for many years.

## ARCTIC AND ALPINE TUNDRAS

The word *tundra* in Russian means "marshy plain." This describes very well much of the level, wet country beyond the timberline in both the Eurasian Arctic and the American Arctic (see Fig. 7-11). This kind of treeless arctic barren, covered with grasses, sedges, lichens, rocks, and water, might be called the "true tundra." The term "tundra" has also been used in a general way to describe any low vegetation beyond timberline, whether arctic or alpine. Even though these vegetation types do not all fit the original definition, the word will be used here to avoid coining new ones to fit each topographic situation that exists beyond timberline.

The arctic tundra forms a broad, treeless ring around the Arctic Ocean and southward to Labrador, Iceland, and southern Greenland. In the North Pacific, it surrounds the Bering Sea from Alaska to Si-

**Fig. 7-11.** *Alpine tundra vegetation of grasses, sedges, and other herbaceous plants with an active solifluction terrace typical of such environments. Beartooth Mountains, Wyoming.*

beria and from the Bering Straits to the Aleutians. There is scarcely a counterpart of the arctic tundra in the Southern Hemisphere because Antarctica is almost completely covered by ice. There are, however, small, widely isolated areas of tundra-like vegetation on some of the subantarctic islands, such as MacQuarie Island south of New Zealand, the Kerguelen Islands in the far southern part of the Indian Ocean, and on South Georgia in the South Atlantic.

*Alpine vegetation* is any low vegetation occurring above timberline on mountains. The derivation of the word is from the European Alps. It is customary, however, to apply the term to the low vegetation on the summit of any high mountain range. Even though one may call this vegetation "alpine tundra," only relatively small areas are tundra-like in the true sense. Much of the vegetation occupies rocky slopes and cliffs, but the best development of alpine vegetation does occur on gently sloping or level areas and resembles arctic tundra in appearance and in the kinds of plants present. In western North America, alpine tundra extends from the Arctic along the great mountain ranges as far south as Mexico. It reappears in somewhat different form in parts of the high Andes of South America. There is also vegetation resembling alpine tundra on many New Zealand mountains and on Mount Kosciusko in Australia. In the Old World, alpine vegetation occurs on almost all the mountain ranges of Europe and Asia. It is at its best on the high slopes of the Alps and other European high mountains. In the Himalayas, alpine plants reach their highest altitudinal limits, 20,000 feet above sea level. The high African volcanoes (Kilimanjaro, Ruwenzori, Kenya, and Elgon) also have alpine vegetation, some of it characterized by tall monument-like Senecios and Lobelias, which resemble certain high altitude Andean plants. There are, however, some truly tundra-like places and plants on these African mountains of the equatorial region.

The climate of the arctic tundra is controlled by the annual cycle of solar radiation. All locations north of the Arctic Circle have several weeks or months during the winter when the sun does not rise above the horizon. Conversely, in the summer there is an equal amount of time when the sun does not set. In winter, the lack of sun coupled with the continuous heat loss from the ground into the dark, clear sky results in a relatively dry and very cold climate, with air temperatures as low as $-70°F$ or more. Although the ground is mostly covered with some snow and ice, there is relatively little snowfall and, of course, no available soil water since it is frozen.

Because of the long days in summer, a fair amount of energy is received from the sun even though the sun is relatively low in the sky. It is enough to melt some of the snow and ice near sea level so that the upper part of the ground becomes wet and there is water available for plant growth. Most of the net radiation is used up in the melting of snow and subsequent evaporation of the water; very little heat is available for heating the air. As a result, air temperatures in the short arctic summer remain low, seldom exceeding $60°F$ except near dry and rocky ground. The plants, however, actually may have higher temperatures than the air because they absorb some of the sun's radiation directly. The higher plant temperature may be helpful in speeding up certain plant processes, such as photosynthesis and respiration.

Alpine climates are similar to those of the Arctic but differ in having some sun during the winter and some nighttime darkness during the summer. Alpine areas also receive more snow, rain, and wind, and have more intense sunlight with a high proportion of ultraviolet. High mountains also receive more high energy cosmic radiation than the immediately surrounding lowlands, even more than is received in the arctic lowlands. However, the greatest amounts of cosmic radiation are received on arctic mountains such as Mount McKinley in Alaska, although there is very little life in these high arctic elevations that would be affected by such strong radiation.

Both arctic and alpine tundra environments are severe. Perhaps the arctic tundra is more severe in winter because there is constant outgoing heat loss and little snow cover. During the growing season, however, the alpine environment, with its wind, high ultraviolet and cosmic radiation, and its cold summer nights, is probably a more rigorous environment.

Tundra soils range from boggy peats through brown loams to rocky and gravelly sands, and may be either wet or dry. Many of the arctic soils, particularly the wet ones, are underlain by permafrost, and only the surface thaws during the brief arctic summer. Permafrost also exists under some boggy alpine soils. Common to both arctic and alpine soils is a conspicuous variety of patterns: stone polygons and nets, soil circles, stone or soil stripes, and terraces. These patterns are due to the thrusting action of repeated freezing and thawing of the wetter soils over solid substrata such as permafrost or rock. The freezing activity tends to sort out the rocks into low, wall-like stripes on hillsides or into polygonal patterns on level ground. Naturally, the result of all this thrusting, sorting, and flowing downhill is a soil instability unlike most soil situations in temperate lands. As a result, tundra vegetation is usually confined to only the more stable parts of the patterns, and there is a great deal of bare soil in the more actively frost-churned places.

Tundra vegetation varies from place to place in the manner in which it covers the ground and the amount of ground it covers. Coverage variations are the results of different combinations of soil frost activity, snow cover, and wind. In general, one can say that the lower the amounts of each of these three factors, the more complete will be the vegetation cover. Under any circumstances, tundra vegetation almost always consists of low, herbaceous, perennial plants. In slight depressions with better protection from the wind there are often dwarf shrubs such as miniature willows and birches. A typical tundra plant is low and compact; this life form allows protection from the wind. The plant's perennial nature allows it to store food one summer for rapid growth during the first part of the following summer. The short cold growing season is unsuited for ordinary annual plants since so little heat is available that seeds may not ripen. The herbaceous habit of these perennials allows buds to be protected from the wind under the soil surface or near the surface under the snow.

The arctic flora is poor in plant species; there are only a few hundred for the entire Arctic compared to over 100,000 for the tropics. The alpine flora of any particular mountain range also usually consists of not more than a few hundred species. However, taken collectively, the flora of all alpine regions would be somewhat richer than the arctic flora. Nevertheless, only a relatively few alpine species can successfully utilize the low heat amounts of tundra environments. A number of these are widespread not only in the Arctic but also in many alpine regions. An arctic-alpine ecologist can feel at home in most tundra regions because it is easy to recognize so many of the species. Floristically, at least, his work is less difficult than that of the tropical ecologist.

We might wonder why some of these species are so widespread. Although the arctic and alpine environments are similar in that they are both cold, there are rather striking differences between them (e.g., the continuous light during the growing season in the arctic compared to the relatively long cold nights of the alpine growing season). There is recent evidence that, in at least some arctic-alpine species, there are latitudinal ecological races. The genetic differences between these races result in different physiological requirements, which adapt the plants to different locations along the latitudinal arctic-alpine gradient.

Almost everywhere in the arctic-alpine floristic area, members of the grass and sedge families are abundant. In addition, there are members of the saxifrage, rose, mustard, buckwheat, and pink families. In these families, more kinds of plants have evolved a tolerance to cold than in families such as the orchids, legumes, mints, and composites, which are principally families of warmer climates.

The above-ground productivity of tundra vegetation is low. Based on the entire year, it is usually less than a gram of dry matter produced per square meter per day; if based on just the short growing season, it is 1 to 4 grams per square meter per day. However, at least as much, and sometimes twice as much, food is transferred to underground parts, such as roots, rhizomes, and bulbs. Thus, total productivity is somewhat higher. Even including underground storage, this is not very much to support animal life if only small areas are considered. However, there are great areas of tundra in the arctic, and since many of the herbivores are migratory, they really depend on the total production of large areas. Such animals as lemmings, caribou, reindeer, and musk-ox move from place to place utilizing forage. Smaller herbivores live on bulbs and rhizomes.

Both vegetational productivity and animal populations seem to follow cycles. An overpopulation of rodents and hares following good vegetational years may be left without food or cover in poor years. In such times, they are ready prey for carnivores (foxes, weasels, owls), which reduce the populations of herbivores with a resultant drop in the populations of carnivores themselves. Little food energy is wasted in a tundra ecosystem until it has been utilized at the carnivore level. Low temperatures tend to help this conservation by keeping fungus and bacterial activity low.

Man has had relatively little effect on arctic tundra ecosystems. The Eskimos have been parts of these natural ecosystems, and have survived or died depending on their ability to get food from these systems. Many Eskimos have also depended largely upon marine ecosystems, which are probably more productive in the Arctic than are the terrestrial systems. The Lapps of northern Europe have brought some of the tundra productivity under partial control by domesticating the arctic reindeer.

Alpine tundras have been equally as unproductive and inhospitable to man as arctic tundras, if not more so. Only a few native peoples have been able to live year round in areas above alpine timberline. Perhaps the best examples are the Sherpas of the Himalayas and the Tibetans. In the European and North American mountains, primitive man avoided the truly alpine areas except during the summer. Alpine areas have, of course, been utilized to some extent as grazing land. This has often led to overgrazing and subsequent destruction of the alpine vegetation. Since alpine plant growth is slow and productivity is low, the numbers and kinds of grazing animals must be adjusted in order to maintain these meadows not only as grazing lands but also as sources of uncontaminated water for lowland use and as places of beauty to be enjoyed by all.

# 8

# ECOLOGY
# AND MAN'S
# WELFARE

It is always difficult, if not impossible, to draw a line between pure and applied science. No one really knows with certainty what knowledge will be applied tomorrow, or in the next century, to improve man's health or to make his economic activities more successful. The difficulty in distinguishing between pure and applied is accentuated in ecology not only because of the complexity of the subject but because man himself is part of the ecosystem. This latter fact, whether consciously recognized or not, has resulted in a strong undercurrent of practicality in ecological research through the years as man has attempted crudely or carefully to manage or modify ecosystems to fit his needs.

Ecological knowledge can be applied at each of the three principal levels of integration—that is, the individual, the population, and the ecosystem.

## APPLIED ECOLOGY OF THE INDIVIDUAL

Every individual organism lives poorly or well as the result of the interactions between its genes and the environment. Just as it is important to know what these genes are and what they control, it is also important to know how the environment regulates gene action and to what extent. A knowledge of the ecology of the individual is basic to all ecology, since populations consist only of individuals and individuals are the biological components of ecosystems. Successful populations and productive ecosystems are summations of good genetic and environmental interaction at the level of the individual. Since the lifetimes of almost all individuals are finite and relatively short, the ecology of any specific individual plant or animal is important to us mainly as it contributes to our knowledge of the ecology of the population or ecosystem to which it belongs. However, if that individual happens to be you, a knowledge of its ecology suddenly assumes tremendous importance.

While any individual human being has a fairly wide environmental tolerance (compared to that of most kinds of organisms), there are limits that differ somewhat from individual to individual. The principle of limiting factors is very much involved in the lives of all of us. Unlike many organisms we can devise all sorts of protections against environmental factors such as low temperatures and lack of water. Even today, however, people do freeze to death in cold regions or die of thirst in the desert. Civilized man has not evolved much genetic tolerance to these environmental extremes; he has learned mainly to devise artificial shields against them. In fact, as a result of natural selection, primitive man may often be better prepared genetically (and also phenotypically) to face rigorous environments than we are. A South African Bushman can survive under desert conditions with almost none of our artifical protections; we could not.

However, there are many things in our personal environments—for example, viruses, certain kinds of radiation—that are so subtle or so new that either we do not recognize them as being adverse to our environmental health or we are just learning how to guard against them. We can feel heat gain or heat loss, see light or rain, and know when we are hungry. But we can be exposed to deadly high energy radiation without knowing it. Lethal viruses may get established in our bodies with few or no symptoms until it is too late. We have only recently learned about high energy radiation and viruses, and we yet have almost no conscious guards against them.

In our everyday life, then, we are continually adjusting to our environments either by internal means or by external protections of our own devising. Better nutrition, medicine, and housing are improving our environmental health conditions; but it is well to remember that man evolved in the absence of many of these environmental protections. As a result of this ameliorated environmental selection pressure, we can imagine the results if some of these protections were taken away.

What we know about temperature tolerance, mineral nutrition, water needs, and light requirements of any species has been built up bit by bit from observations and measurements of individual organisms. Since most individuals within a species vary genetically and environments also vary, we cannot be absolutely precise in predicting the ecological behavior of, for example, a single blue spruce tree in Boulder Creek Canyon in Colorado without some observations on that particular tree. But from past observations of many individuals of the same species, we know something of what results to expect with blue spruce in any given geographic region. Thus, a knowledge of the ecology of the individual is fundamental to a knowledge of the ecology of populations and also to the ecology of ecosystems.

## APPLIED ECOLOGY OF POPULATIONS

A population, it will be recalled, is a group of genetically related individuals. If it is a relatively small group in a relatively small geographic area with the possibility of easy pollen exchange, it is called a local population. If it is a large number of individuals in several local populations distributed over a relatively large geographic region, it is an ecological race or even a species. Some species, of course, are made up of only a few local populations or even just one, but most species consist of many such populations and may have a large geographic range.

Considerable use can be made of knowledge of the environmental tolerance ranges of populations, races, and species of plants and animals. Tolerance range information can be obtained from field environmental and growth data in the regions where the organisms actually grow, or by experimentally subjecting many individuals of the species to a series of environmental combinations in gardens, greenhouses, or controlled environment chambers. In a general way, a great store of information has been gathered through the years by gardeners, agriculturalists, plant physiologists, and ecologists on the ecological tolerance ranges of many species and varieties of cultivated plants and of weeds. Somewhat less and more scattered information is available for some species of wild plants, including trees. For most plant species, little or no information exists on tolerance ranges.

The field of tolerance range ecology or comparative physiological ecology is a challenging area of ecology. Tolerance range information, to be widely applicable, must be obtained from as wide a geographic representation of genetic biotypes within the species as possible. In turn, the degree of genetic variation within the local populations of the species should be known. It is genetic variation and the frequency with which new genetic forms appear that determine whether or not a species can tolerate the extreme range of environmental conditions concomitant with broad geographic range, or the suddenly severe conditions likely to occur as a result of man's activities.

Rapid transportation around the world and ease of scientific communication now make it possible to obtain the seeds or other living material of many species easily and quickly. These plants can be grown and measured in "phytotrons" or controlled environment chambers for relatively rapid and quantitative assessment of tolerance range limits and optimal growth conditions.

Tolerance range information is fundamental to an understanding of actual and potential geographic range limits of any species. The actual geographic range of a species consists of the places where it occurs now. This actual range provides environmental conditions that lie within the limits set by the tolerance range. However, there may be other geographic areas that also have conditions suitable for individuals of the same species, but for one reason or another the species does not occur there. Barriers such as oceans or deserts may have prevented its getting there. The species may have been there in the past but was eliminated by temporarily adverse conditions and has not had time to migrate back or barriers have prevented it. Or it may be a young species and time has been insufficient to allow it to migrate to all suitable and reachable areas. In fact, very few species of plants and animals occupy their potential geographic ranges—that is, all places where the environment is suitable as determined by the tolerance range of the species.

Most species never completely occupy their potential geographic ranges because of inherently poor dispersal mechanisms, which operate too slowly to keep ahead of changing environments. Since the earth has a history of continually changing environmental conditions, the potential geographic range of any species is also continually changing as new potential environments open up and others close.

Migrations and changing environments have always been a part of the earth's ecological history. The fossil record of tropical breadfruit trees in Oregon and redwoods in the Nevada desert, for example, is good evidence of this. Man, by migrating into practically his entire potential geographic range, consciously or accidentally has made possible the rapid migrations and invasions of many kinds of weedy plants and animals. The more rapid man's environmental changes are, the more likely the only survivors will be the genetically plastic and adaptable "weeds."

At the population level, ecology is of great practical importance in understanding, predicting, and controlling invasions by unwanted but adaptable organisms (i.e., weeds), which with man's help are moving rapidly into their potential geographic ranges. One can think of hundreds of examples of such organisms introduced into new areas either accidentally or purposely but with disastrous results. Quarantines of all kinds have been set up, but it is almost impossible to stop this explosive tide of pathogenic fungi and bacteria, voracious or disease-carrying insects, weedy plants, and noxious animals. Our own American chestnut tree has been eliminated by the chestnut blight fungus introduced accidentally from China. The American elm similarly appears doomed because of the Dutch elm disease fungus and phloem necrosis. European weeds crowd out our native plants; the European starling does the same with our native birds. On the other side of the Atlantic, the American muskrat has spread in tremendous numbers throughout Europe and from there into Asia.

Man has succeeded in a relatively short time, by providing rapid transportation over barriers and by modifying environments, in allowing adaptable organisms to establish great new populations far from their original haunts or to increase population sizes in their own native ecosystems. At the same time, other less aggressive and less adaptable species are dying out. Most of this, of course, we would like to prevent for both practical and aesthetic reasons. A knowledge of ecological tolerance ranges would help us to control potentially widespread species and to save those dangerously near extinction. Conservation and control based on sound ecological knowledge of both populations and ecosystems is the only course we can follow.*

The other side of the coin is brighter, namely, the introduction and environmental adaptation of crop plants and ornamentals. Much of what we know of crop ecology comes, of course, from long ago. On the other hand, scientific investigation of crop tolerance ranges in the last 50 years has allowed extension of the productive ranges of a number of species and the introduction of many new plants into cultivation in environments suitable to them. With the increase in world human population and only a limited amount of arable land, it is imperative that we get all possible information on tolerance ranges of existing and potential crop species.

## APPLIED ECOLOGY OF ECOSYSTEMS

Important as applied population ecology is, it is only a part of the much more complex problems that must be faced in ecosystem ecology. Because of the holocoenotic nature of the environment and the corollary situation of trigger-factor action, man can manipulate whole ecosystems for his benefit. With even less difficulty, he can let them get completely out of hand, to the detriment of both present and future generations. In a modern, crowded, and touchy world, a knowledge of ecosystem interactions, trends, and possibilities is absolutely neces-

* For an interesting discussion of the interactions between "weedy" and native species, see Elton (1958).

sary to our future well-being. Unfortunately, ecosystems are likely to be large and complex and not always subject to easy experimentation. This factor makes reliable information on the ecology of particular ecosystems difficult to obtain from the standpoint of cost and time. Moreover, there is a lack of people accustomed and trained to think at the ecosystem level. Fortunately, however, we do have some rather well-established ecological principles as guides and some detailed information on how certain ecosystems behave. In the future, use of small model ecosystems or even electrical analog ecosystems and high-speed computers may help us understand and predict the happenings in changing ecosystems.

Although ecosystems are of all sizes and types, perhaps we can simplify the array into five levels of natural ecosystems:

1. Local ecosystems
2. Formational ecosystems
3. Continental or ocean-basin ecosystems
4. The earth ecosystem
5. The solar ecosystem

*Local ecosystems* are ecosystems of various kinds and sizes which, while primarily self-supporting, may have some export and import of energy and materials by way of wide-ranging large animals or by atmospheric or water currents. Examples of local ecosystems would be a pine forest, a patch of prairie, or a lake.

*Formational ecosystems* correspond to the large vegetational formations or zones on a single continent. All the local ecosystems within the geographic limits of a formational ecosystem participate to some extent in its energy flow and cycling of materials.

*Continental or ocean-basin ecosystems* are made up of all the formation ecosystems between which there is some circulation of energy and materials because of the lack of any really large natural land or sea barrier.

The *earth ecosystem* is made up of all living things on earth and their environments.

The *solar ecosystem* consists of the whole solar system, which derives its energy from the sun and which could include possible life on other planets or their satellites. Up to now, the flow of radiant energy outward from the sun and back into space as radiation or reflection from the planets is the principal interchange within the solar ecosystem. However, with man-made satellites and space probes, circulation, however sporadic, of another type has been initiated. Cosmic radiation and meteorites, of course, indicate the flow of matter into the solar ecosystem from our galaxy and from even beyond, meaning that even larger ecosystems exist.

In addition to these natural ecosystems, in which man's effects have been relatively casual or accidental, there are modified ecosystems, in which man deliberately changes parts of natural ecosystems so that a considerable part of the productivity can be channeled to his immediate use. Examples are managed forests and rangeland, farm ponds, and cultivated crops.

Modern cities and space satellites, both of which require life-support systems for the inhabitants, can be classed as synthetic or artificial ecosystems.

## EFFECT OF MAN ON NATURAL ECOSYSTEMS

Primitive man, at least when his numbers were small, lived in the ecosystem without essentially destroying it. His eventual use of fire and the beginnings of agriculture introduced far-reaching trigger factors into natural ecosystems and the beginnings of purposefully modified systems. In recent centuries, this combination has resulted in a tremendous channeling of food energy into human populations. The resultant population explosion has required even more modification of natural ecosystems, either purposely or inadvertently.

Since ecosystems are holocoenotic, the effects of increasing human populations are seen not only in obvious ecosystem destruction and replacement but also eventually in the more subtle and long-range effects of trigger factors. As human numbers increase, there is, of course, a constantly increasing shift from natural ecosystems to modified ecosystems. All precautions should be taken to avoid introducing unnecessary trigger factors into either natural or modified ecosystems. Such factors could result in such a drastic imbalance in the local ecosystem that man's immediate welfare is endangered and chains of events may result in unfavorable ecosystem changes far beyond the local situation, even to the level of the earth ecosystem. It is difficult to imagine such far-reaching unplanned reactions as being beneficial to man's continued welfare.

Until recent decades, destruction of natural ecosystems by man's encroachment was taken as a matter of course. It was something that came along with civilization whether or not man needed the land for agriculture or for just a quick harvest of certain natural resources. Examples are numerous: the cutting, burning, and abandonment of forest land; overhunting and elimination of big grazing animals such as the bison in North America and the okapi in Africa; the overgrazing and deterioration of natural grasslands in America, Europe, Asia, and Australia. Once climax vegetation and animal life is destroyed or seriously altered over large areas, it is almost impossible for them to return without man's help. There simply are not enough parent individuals to replenish large areas before other organisms gain control of the environment.

Destruction of vegetational cover usually results in accelerated erosion, flooding, and silting. An overgrazed watershed may yield more water than a well-vegetated one. However, the water comes off erratically, often in floods, with destruction by erosion to the headwater areas and damage by silting and boulders in the valleys. The result is destruction of or damage to the aquatic ecosystems of rivers and lakes. Water pollution by sewage or factory wastes also drastically modifies these aquatic systems.

More subtle in their effects on natural ecosystems are the introductions or invasions by noxious plants or animals, which by their aggressiveness make places for themselves at the expense of the native biota. These pests and weeds, because of their greater genetic adaptability and high reproductive rates, are better able than climax species to adjust to man's environmental modifications. Ecological management of the land can eliminate many of these pests but often this is slow. More rapid results may be obtained with pesticides (insecticides and herbicides); however, here again, more or less unknown variables are introduced into the ecosystem. When the pesticide effects spread far beyond the immediate targets, great damage may be done to other organisms, man included. Although pesticides are useful in modern land management, they may create more ecological problems than they solve. Proper ecological management of an area should lead eventually to domination by the organisms we want to encourage. In some instances, rapid evolution has produced well-adapted ecological races of weeds, which survive in spite of good ecologic practice. In such cases, pesticides may be justified for turning the ecosystem back in the desired direction.

Biological control of weeds and noxious insects and other animals by the careful introduction of specific predators or parasites has worked well in many places. The more specific the attacking organism the better, since there is less chance of the ever present danger of the cure being worse than the disease. However, since the controlling organisms are always further up the food chain than the pest, their ecological control is likely to be easier.

Insect control by radiation sterilization of males or by use of a sex-attractant chemical has been shown to be practical and specific. Such methods would make unnecessary the possible ecological damage of widespread insecticides.

In most cases, natural ecosystems have evolved under relatively low levels of background high energy radiation. Since 1945, there have been many increases in background radiation, primarily because of fallout and radioactive waste disposal. This radiation increase has not been uniform in time or place. No one knows what the eventual effects of this trigger factor will be, even if no further increases occur—and this seems unlikely. Experiments have shown that organisms differ in their sensitivity to high energy radiation. If a pine-oak forest, for example, is exposed to low but chronic levels of such radiation, the pines will be damaged before the oaks. Forest ecosystems as a whole appear to be more susceptible than grassland ecosystems. Selective change in ecosystem composition and operation would be an inevitable result of large radiation doses.

Besides the direct effects of additional high energy radiation on ecosystems, the incorporation of radioactive isotopes from fallout and reactor wastes into the ecosystem food web tends to concentrate these isotopes in dangerous quantities in organisms near the top of the food chain. The concentrating organism often happens to be man. Strontium 90, iodine 131, and cesium 137 are examples of such dangerous isotopes. The study of the pathways of these isotopes through ecosystems and the effects of chronic but increased radiation levels in ecosystems is of great practical importance and has led to the considerable work now being done in radiation ecology.

Dramatic in its impact on natural and modified ecosystems of all kinds is the rise of the "giant city ecosystem." For man's convenience and needs, the biota and soil have been stripped away to be replaced by steel, concrete, stone, wood, brick, and glass. Only the climatic part of the original ecosystem remains, and this is so modified locally by the different heat budgets of concrete and brick, the greatly increased runoff from roofs, parking lots, and road, and the smoke and fumes produced by chimneys and automobiles as sometimes to be scarcely recognizable. The natural ecosystems are gone in the big cities, and in their places we have a synthetic or artificial ecosystem which has evolved through the centuries and has certain advantages for us.

Man, however, did not originate in such a system, and many of us are not well adapted to the new physical environment of smoke and smog, heat and cold, great numbers of people, and the absence of the green of vegetation. By fashioning and maintaining a continual supply of energy from outside the system, man can exist as a species in such places. However, certain individuals may not do well in such an environment. Natural selection gradually could produce an urban ecological race or races in man just as industrialization has produced adapted races in birds, insects, and plants that live in such environments.

## MODIFIED ECOSYSTEMS

Man early in his history found that a little disturbance of the land increased the yield of certain plants that he used for food or other needs. By obtaining a little more light from cutting or burning the forests, the Iroquois found they could help their corn crop; a little chopping with primitive hoes lessened the competitive effects of weeds. Even today, some inhabitants of tropical regions merely hack away at the scrub and forest in order to maintain just enough disturbed area so that they can scatter seeds of various food plants in random fashion. Agriculture had its beginnings in disturbed areas around the huts or tents of primitive man; in these open places weeds thrived also, and, in fact, edible weeds probably were the first cultivated plants. Actually, it does not take a great deal of hit or miss cultivation to greatly increase the yield of edible plant products over what can be obtained in undisturbed ecosystems. Here, then, man modifies an ecosystem, takes it out of its steady state, and gets some sort of harvestable crop.

As the centuries went by, man became more sophisticated in knowing just how much to modify an ecosystem in order to increase the yield of whatever plant he wanted to harvest. Since certain food and fiber plants were in most demand, it was found soon that the yield could be increased greatly by getting rid of all competition from other plants and eliminating as much damage as possible from birds, insects, and wild mammals. Soil fertilization, even though casual, also increased the yield. During the nineteenth century, scientific agriculture began to come into its own; today the yields from greatly modified crop ecosystems are many times as large as could be obtained from the primitive ancestral systems. An agronomist is actually a crop ecologist; his success depends upon the knowledge he has of the principles and data of population and ecosystem ecology for his particular crops.

Modification of forest, range, pasture, and aquatic ecosystems has not proceeded quite as far as "pure-stand" crop ecology. However, if it becomes necessary to increase the yield of these natural and seminatural ecosystems, modification must come, and must come as a result of scientific management based on ecological principles.

As a general rule, ecological management of forests or pastures appears to be adopted first where large but relatively prosperous human populations demand much from small areas. These people can afford to gamble on experimental manipulation of small patches of these ecosystems where the gains will likely be many times the cost of the experiment. For over 200 years, this type of scientific approach has been followed in the management of the forests and pastures of western Europe, and with very good results. In America, the abundance of our relatively large and untouched natural resources held back scientific forest, range, and pasture work until the demands of the twentieth century made such ecological management imperative. We are now beginning to catch up scientifically in the management of these wild and semiwild lands. Forest, range, pasture, wildlife, and aquatic ecologists are all contributing to an understanding of how such ecosystems can be managed for increased and sustained yield without damage to the soil and water resources. In many parts of the world, however, the long and increasingly dense occupancy by man had already caused extensive ecosystem damage and poverty before scientific land management developed. It is in these places that the big test of ecosystem management will come, namely, the test of rebuilding productive forest and range ecosystems where suitable environments have all but been destroyed by man's overactivity.

## SYNTHETIC ECOSYSTEMS

Synthetic ecosystems are either completely man-made or almost so. To make a model synthetic ecosystem, one first creates an environment out of a suitable light and heat energy source, a substratum of nutrients and solvent (usually water), and either ordinary air or a gas mixture to provide an atmosphere. Green plants are then added to provide the first or carbon-fixing trophic level. Herbivorous animals, carnivorous animals, and decomposers are needed for a completely cycling synthetic system.

A good example of a synthetic ecosystem is the balanced aquarium flourishing under artificial light in the laboratory. Such an aquarium ecosystem can be used as a model in many kinds of ecological experiments. Small terrarium systems can also be built and used, although processes are somewhat more difficult to measure here than in the aquarium.

A step beyond these simple systems are the sharply demarcated synthetic ecosystems in which man is a participating member (e.g., a submarine or airplane, or a space vehicle). In a submarine or airplane, finite amounts of raw materials are stored aboard at the start of the trip and the ecosystem becomes operative when the hatches close. Little or no attempt is made at recycling carbon, oxygen, water, or minerals, and no new energy source is received from outside. This restricts the operative time to a finite period determined by the exhaustion of the supply of a vital material.

Earth distances are moderate; space distances, of course, are not. For example, a round trip to the moon would take at least five days, and a round trip to Venus would take more than eight months. Moreover, since tremendous thrust energies are required to free a space vehicle from the earth's gravitational field, the vehicle must be as small as possible and yet be capable of supporting life for the duration of the trip with perhaps time to spare. For a few days, a man can get along with relatively little addition of food energy if oxygen and water are recycled or added and carbon dioxide removed or broken down. However, for a trip of six months to a year, an efficient, self-sufficient ecosystem is needed in which solar energy can be captured and stored as food energy, carbon dioxide removed and replaced with molecular oxygen, and water and minerals recycled. All of this must be done simply in a small space strictly demarcated and shielded from the unfavorable aspects of the space environment, and yet utilizing the solar energy so abundant there. Even one man requires enough energy, minerals, and water in a year's time to make the design of his life-support system or synthetic ecosystem extremely difficult. The support of several people in such an enclosed ecosystem in space provides even more problems in terms of logistics.

## CONSERVATION AND ECOLOGY

All of us have heard that natural resources should be conserved or saved. Perhaps this idea should be examined critically. Why, in fact, should natural resources be conserved?

First, it is well to remember that almost all of the earth's ecosystem types evolved before man was much of a dominant ecological force. As man increased the frequency of fire, cleared the land, increased his hunting, and grew crops, his own population increased steadily and, in time, exponentially. The result of this tremendous increase in population has been the disruption of many of these balanced ecosystems with the diversion of energy and matter into the human population. Since little thought was given in the past to the need for supporting increasingly greater numbers of people, these ecosystems usually were hurriedly exploited without heed to permanent damage or future productivity, or to scientific considerations. The rapid shift of energy and materials to domestic animals and to man resulted in radically altering the balance between the environment and the vegetation that supported all other life. Trigger factors, apparent or nonapparent, started reactions that changed ecosystems, often so drastically that they were replaced by new and less desirable systems. Sometimes the vegetation of even these man-adapted ecosystems was destroyed, so that not only did productivity cease but even the soil was left unprotected, and disappeared under the erosive forces of wind or rain. All of this was made even more serious by the constantly greater demands of the increasing human populations. Population pressure in the eastern Mediterranean lands resulted in widespread overgrazing by goats and sheep and the eventual loss of much of the natural vegetation and soil. Eventually only the barren, unproductive rock remained, with consequent impoverishment and malnutrition of the people. In southwestern Asia, similar overgrazing on sandy soils resulted in the wind's undermining the little remaining vegetation and blowing the topsoil away, and the land became a waste of shifting desert-like dunes.

Much of this type of destruction occurred before there was a realization of what was happening and before the ecological principles of productive land management were known. By the middle of the eighteenth century, the imminent disappearance of the last European forests compelled the adoption of methods designed to save the remaining forests and to stimulate forest productivity to meet future needs. This beginning of modern forestry greatly increased the amount of available timber in Europe. Continued scientific development there provided the basis for forest conservation and practice in other, more recently settled parts of the earth.

Until the twentieth century, continued discovery and opening up of new lands to be exploited saved man from his own ecological errors. In Siberia, North America, and in the tropics, this exploitation has continued into present times. However, it is accompanied now by scientific management which, though crude by European standards, constitutes recognition of the fact that such virgin lands are far too valuable to allow destruction of their environmental assets.

The fact that the standard of living in many parts of the world is extremely low is partly due to the past destruction of the irreplaceable resources of soil and the balanced natural landscape. To some extent also it is due to improper or inefficient use of resources that are still adequate but that could be made more productive by proper management and utilization. If the earth's population continues to increase in its present dramatic manner, all possible ecosystem productivity must be efficiently channeled to man's use, or living standards as far as food and shelter are concerned will go down. In other words, the energy, mineral, and water cycles must be efficiently and wisely used without waste or leakage. However, if human populations do grow unchecked to such sizes as to require most of the world's productivity, we may have achieved nothing but crowding and loss of space. Even under these highly unlikely conditions, populations must level off eventually because certain factors (now perhaps unknown) will become limiting.

All organisms including man are dependent upon environmental resources for food energy and also for raw materials such as water and certain minerals. Civilized man has also become dependent on materials for clothing and shelter. Many of these latter materials are produced agriculturally or synthesized in factories; without them, modern man would have a difficult time in most environments.

Some of the resources that we need from the environment are virtually inexhaustible. Others are exhaustible but can be maintained or renewed with proper ecological forethought and management. Still others, if improperly handled, can be exhausted permanently. Table 8-1 is a generalized outline of resources indicating the degree of their exhaustibility and renewability.

Table 8-1*

| Inexhaustible Resources | Exhaustible but Renewable Resources | Exhaustible and Irreplaceable Resources |
|---|---|---|
| Total amounts of:<br>  Atmosphere<br>  Water<br>  Rock<br>  Solar energy | Water in usable condition<br>†Vegetation<br>†Animal life<br>†Human populations<br>Certain soil minerals<br>Uncontaminated $CO_2$<br>  and $O_2$ where needed<br>Certain ecosystem types | Soil<br>Certain minerals<br>Rare species<br>Certain ecosystem<br>  types<br>Landscape in<br>  natural condition<br>Much of the ground-<br>  water supply |

* Adapted from Costin (1959).

† The original genetic composition is impossible to duplicate except in known varieties of cultivated crops. Also, parent stock must be available and able to migrate into the area or the offspring must be able to migrate.

The total amounts of water, air, and rock on earth are finite, but the quantities are so great that under existing conditions of temperature there will always be enough to meet our needs. However, local or temporary shortages of specific inorganic resources can and do occur. Moreover, most of the water on earth is saline; it is converted back to fresh water only by the solar still of the hydrologic cycle, and will run back to the oceans again very quickly unless there are natural or artificial obstacles in its way. Although water itself is inexhaustible in total amount, *fresh* water is not—particularly in the places where it is needed most—that is, where it is a limiting factor.

While fresh water is exhaustible, it can be maintained near where it is needed by proper ecological management of the watershed or by dams and reservoirs. If exhausted, surface and soil supplies of water will be renewed sooner or later by the giant natural still of the hydrologic cycle. This is not necessarily true for ground-water supplies, however.

Because the reproductive capacity of most plants and animals is relatively high, there can be a certain amount of recovery of the vegetation and animal life of most ecosystems if damage has not been too severe or if total destruction has been confined to relatively small areas. Usually, however, such a renewal of biotic resources will result in somewhat different vegetation and animal populations because there may be a local extinction of certain species or genotypes. Also, swings in climatic cycles may result in unfavorable growing conditions for some of the kinds of organisms that were parts of the original ecosystem. A small area devastated by a forest fire will be revegetated quickly through successional stages because undestroyed seed sources are nearby. A large burned area will revegetate very slowly because nearby seed sources will have been destroyed, and migration over any considerable distance takes time. Large devastated areas also are more likely to be exposed to relatively severe environmental conditions since there will be a lack of vegetation to protect against wind, drying out, and erosion. When vegetation is destroyed over a large area, the lack of nearby seed sources and local environmental changes may hold back succession so long that the general climate may have time to change or, even worse, the soil may erode away. The Tillamook burn of 1933 on the Oregon coast was so large that revegetation has been very slow; smaller burns have revegetated much more quickly.

Fresh unpolluted air is another exhaustible but renewable resource. Both people and plants do poorly in air polluted with smoke, hydrocarbons, smog, sulfur fumes, and many other abnormal constituents. Most pollution has resulted from the burning of fossil fuels (coal and oil and their products) in industry, homes, and automobiles. Some pollution is the result of other industrial processes. Pollution can be particularly bad where large cities occupy topographic basins where a relatively shallow layer of cool air is trapped under warm air by an inversion. The smog of the Los Angeles metropolitan area is the result of this combination. Fortunately, fresh unpolluted air is still abundant throughout the earth as a whole. In local situations, polluted air can be replaced with fresh air if the sources of contamination are eliminated. Natural atmospheric circulation assures us of the replenishment of pure air anywhere on earth provided we keep contaminants out of it.

In contrast to these exhaustible but renewable resources, some essential parts of our environment are irreplaceable if lost. Chief among these is the soil because soil is the immediate source of essential mineral elements and water for plant growth. Plants can be grown without soil in nutrient solution tanks or small containers but this is economically and practically unsound on a large scale. Without soil we would be without food.

Soil is the product of climate and vegetation working slowly on the geologic substratum over thousands of years. It can be destroyed by erosion in a matter of a few months or a few years. Once gone it cannot be replaced even with man's modern industrial and scientific ingenuity. Even long-term contamination by fallout, certain organic chemicals, or salts can take soil out of productive use for a long time. This is particularly true of salting in poorly drained irrigated areas. Of all the necessary environmental resources, the soil is the one we can least afford to lose. With soil a region can be made productive even at the cost of some ingenuity and effort; without the soil, the region can only be unproductive rock, no matter what other environmental attributes it may have. Water without soil does not result in productivity. Furthermore, surface water is renewable; soil is not. The ancient civilizations of the Middle East, where water was scarce, understood water conservation but failed to protect their soils and vegetation. The result was famine and economic disaster.

Almost inseparable from the problem of soil conservation is the problem of landscape conservation. By "landscape" is meant the total ecosystem-topographic complex of a region or area. By vegetational destruction, erosion, and the resultant deposition of silt and sand, man had already succeeded in destroying many landscapes long before the mid-twentieth century. The development of great earth-moving machines and concrete technology have made possible the rapid growth of great metropolitan centers connected by superhighways. At the same time this massive earth-moving is permanently changing the landscape. Each new highway over the Sierra Nevada, for example, produces a new and unsightly scar. It is necessary for engineers to become familiar with the irreversible ecological consequences of landscape alteration and make plans not only for the economic needs of the moment but also for future consequences both economic and aesthetic.

Another example of permanent landscape alteration is the silting up of reservoirs, lakes, depressions, and lowlands because of accelerated erosion in the headwaters. It is relatively easy to move earth downhill but tremendously costly and impractical to move it out of these depressions. Good dam and reservoir sites are not particularly common. When reservoirs are rendered useless by silting, any possible advantage of changing the landscape with a dam in the first place has been lost due to poor land use upstream.

There is another aspect of landscape conservation that has even wider implications: scientific, aesthetic, recreational, economic. This is the preservation of enough wilderness areas to meet future needs. Scientifically, we need to know how these natural ecosystems work. We will never get this information if they are destroyed.

Aesthetically and recreationally, many of these wild areas, particularly in mountains and along seashores, provide man's only escape from the pressures and cares of overpopulated urban existence. These values are difficult to measure in terms of money but they are nevertheless real. The question is, do we want to live in a completely man-modified world? If there is some value in knowing and appreciating the kinds of original wild ecosystems, there is no time to lose. They must be protected now; they are irreplaceable.

On a smaller scale, but also a part of the larger picture of ecosystem preservation, is the conservation of the genetic stocks of rare species of plants and animals. The evolution of these species took thousands and millions of years. In one way or another, man has eliminated many species in the last several thousand years and even more in the last century. The mammoth and mastodon, those giant elephants, were part of our North American fauna when man first arrived here; they have been gone for only a few thousand years. Did man hasten this extinction? Flint spearpoints found with the skeletons of mammoths indicate that he may have helped. We know that man eliminated the giant moas, birds much larger than ostriches, in New Zealand only a few centuries ago. We know, too, that man completely killed off the untold millions of passenger pigeons in eastern North America within the last 125 years. He almost did the same to the American bison, reducing its numbers from millions to a few hundreds in the space of a few decades and upsetting the economy of the Plains Indians. Apparently, it is not only the rare species that are in danger, although a rare species is more likely to be susceptible.

Extinction by man has been the fate not only of many animal

species but of numerous plant species. Some of these have been relatively widespread like the American chestnut; some were of restricted occurrence, such as the Santa Cruz tarweed (*Holocarpha macradenia*) in California, which was destroyed habitat and all by bulldozers. Actually, several rare California plant species have probably become extinct because their special habitats have been destroyed by the spread of cities and highways.

Aside from the purely aesthetic loss, there is also a practical side to species conservation. This is concerned with the loss of genetic stock of possible scientific value or of possible usefulness in the breeding of new varieties of plants or animals. Once these genetic stocks are gone, there is usually little chance of getting them back. This is certainly true where there are no close relatives of the extinct form. Where close relatives do exist, it is sometimes possible by repeated crossing and selection to re-create the extinct form. Some German scientists, after many years of work, re-created the extinct European aurochs, the golden cattle of prehistoric times, starting with the genes still present in domestic cattle.

While species extinction because of inability to adjust to changing environments is an age-old phenomenon, it may not be ecologically wise to hasten along this process by our own carelessness. In addition to the drabness of living in a monotonously uniform biological world of a few crop plants, a few kinds of domestic animals, and a few widespread weeds, there is also danger in uniformity. Disease organisms, which are continually evolving new and virulent forms, could completely wipe out a uniform variety or species that had no biologic resistance to the attack. Moreover, there is, apparently, greater ecosystem stability or homeostasis in communities with a great variety of kinds of organisms. Charles Elton in *Ecology of Invasions* suggested that the very complexity of the tropical rain forest, with its great numbers of species occupying all sorts of ecological niches, tends to keep any one species from outbreaks of numbers which could disrupt the system. For example, insect outbreaks in such forests are almost unknown because there are always so many enemies and parasites ready to utilize this new food supply. However, in the relatively uniform and relatively new coniferous forests of the north there are not always enough natural checks and balances to contain outbreaks of insects such as the spruce budworm or the pine bark beetle. Moreover, the uniform nature of the dominant trees in such forests often results in spectacular destruction. Consequently, we must preserve genetic, and thus ecological, diversity in a community if we want continued biological stability in the future.

Further evidence on the effect of biological heterogeneity in maintaining stability can be found in *Plants, Man and Life* by Edgar Anderson. He describes the casual and heterogeneous Indian gardens of Central America which are made up of many kinds of plants—trees, shrubs, vines, and herbs—all growing together in apparently hit or miss fashion. But this very complexity keeps out weeds and prevents outbreaks of noxious insects. Similar tangled gardens are found throughout the primitive tropics; they may look unsightly and ill-kempt to northern eyes but they succeed where neatly ordered weed-free rows would be difficult to maintain, would leave the soil open to erosion and drought, and would make the garden more susceptible to insect attacks.

Finally, we should remember that, in spite of our ingenuity, we are able to live on earth because the *whole* physical and biological environment is still favorable to us. We would like to keep it that way. Dinosaurs fitted their environment too, but they were powerless to do anything about complex environmental changes or to evolve genetically adapted forms quickly enough to meet changing conditions, and thereby became extinct. Many other animals have become extinct too, some quite recently. In spite of our numbers, the same thing can happen to man. Because trigger factors in the environment sometimes act so subtly, we may not realize what is happening until too late. We can be sure that checks and balances in the earth ecosystem will result eventually in some kind of ecological homeostasis; but man may not be a part of the new system. It is up to us to understand our environment and to preserve it as much as possible from the introduction of potentially dangerous factors. No other organism has ever had that choice.

## ECOLOGY AS A UNIFYING SCIENCE

Most scientists are concerned with the study of fundamental knowledge of parts of ecosystems—atoms, molecules, cells, tissues, organisms, minerals, weather, energy. Only ecologists study whole ecosystems. Since ecosystems are large and complex units of study, the ecologist cannot afford to be much of a specialist. He must be a generalist who fits the fundamental discoveries of the specialists into an understanding of a functioning ecosystem. In a world of uncertain existence and changing environments, there is need for the broad view of the ecologist and his knowledge of holocoenotic ecosystems. Perhaps this is the greatest contribution that ecology can make to our common welfare.

# SUGGESTIONS FOR

# FURTHER READING

Anderson, E. *Plants, Man and Life*. Boston: Little, Brown & Company, 1952.

Asprey, G. F., and R. G. Robbins. "The Vegetation of Jamaica." *Ecological Monographs*, Vol. 23, pp. 359–412, 1953.

Billings, W. D. "The Environmental Complex in Relation to Plant Growth and Distribution." *Quarterly Review of Biology*, Vol. 27, pp. 251–265, 1952.

Bliss, L. C. "Net Primary Production of Tundra Ecosystems." In *Die Stoffproduktion der Pflanzendecke*, ed. H. Leith. Stuttgart: Gustav Fischer Verlag, 1962.

Budyko, M. I. *The Heat Balance of the Earth's Surface*, trans. N. A. Stepanova. U.S. Weather Bureau, U.S. Department of Commerce, 1958.

Cain, S. A. *Foundations of Plant Geography*. New York: Harper & Row, Inc., 1944.

Cain, S. A., and G. M. de O. Castro. *Manual of Vegetation Analysis*. New York: Harper & Row, Inc., 1959.

Carson, R. L. *Silent Spring*. Boston: Houghton Mifflin Co., 1962.

Clausen, J. *Stages in the Evolution of Plant Species*. Ithaca, N.Y.: Cornell University Press, 1951.

Cole, L. C. "The Ecosphere." *Scientific American*, Vol. 198, pp. 83–92, 1958.

Cooper, C. F. "The Ecology of Fire." *Scientific American*, Vol. 204, pp. 150–160, 1961.

Costin, A. G. "Replaceable and Irreplaceable Resources and Land Use." *Journal of the Australian Institute of Agricultural Science*. Vol. 25, pp. 3–9, 1959.

Dasmann, R.F. *The Last Horizon*. New York: The Macmillan Company, 1963.

Daubenmire, R. F. *Plants and Environment*, 2nd ed. New York: John Wiley & Sons., Inc., 1959.

Elton, C. S. *The Ecology of Invasions by Animals and Plants*. London: Methuen & Company, Ltd., 1958.

Eyre, S. R. *Vegetation and Soils: A World Picture*. London: Edward Arnold, Ltd., 1963.

Gates, D. M. *Energy Exchange in the Biosphere*. New York: Harper & Row, Inc., 1962.

Geiger, R. *The Climate Near the Ground*, trans. M. N. Stewart et al. Cambridge, Mass.: Harvard University Press, 1957.

Golley, F. B. "Energy Dynamics of a Food Chain of an Old-Field Community." *Ecological Monographs,* Vol. 30, pp. 187–206, 1960.

Good, R. *The Geography of the Flowering Plants,* 2nd ed. London: Longmans, Green & Company, 1953.

Graham, E. H. *Natural Principles of Land Use.* New York: Oxford University Press, 1944.

Greig-Smith, P. *Quantitative Plant Ecology.* London: Butterworth's Scientific Publication, 1957.

Harper, J. L. "Approaches to the Study of Plant Competition." In *Symposia of the Society for Experimental Biology,* 15, "Mechanisms in Biological Competition," 1961.

Heslop-Harrison, J. *New Concepts in Flowering-Plant Taxonomy.* Cambridge, Mass.: Harvard University Press, 1956.

Marr, J. W. *Ecosystems of the East Slope of the Front Range in Colorado,* University of Colorado Series in Biology, No. 8. Boulder, Colo.: University of Colorado Press, 1961.

Merriam, C. H. "Results of a Biological Survey of the San Francisco Mountain Region and the Desert of the Little Colorado, Arizona." *North American Fauna,* No. 3, pp. 1–136, 1890.

Mooney, H. A., and W. D. Billings. "Comparative Physiological Ecology of Arctic and Alpine Populations of *Oxyria digyna." Ecological Monographs,* Vol. 31, pp. 1–29, 1961.

Newell, N. D. "Crises in the History of Life." *Scientific American,* Vol. 208, pp. 76–92, 1963.

Odum, E. P. *Fundamentals of Ecology,* 2nd ed. Philadelphia: W. B. Saunders Company, 1959.

Oosting, H. J. *The Study of Plant Communities,* 2nd ed. San Francisco: W. H. Freeman & Co., 1956.

Ovington, J. D., D. Heitkamp, and D. B. Lawrence. "Plant Biomass and Productivity of Prairie, Savanna, Oakwood, and Maize Field Ecosystems in Central Minnesota." *Ecology,* Vol. 44, pp. 52–63, 1963.

Phillips, E. A. *Methods of Vegetation Study.* New York: Holt, Rinehart & Winston, Inc., 1959.

Schimper, A. F. W. *Plant-Geography upon a Physiological Basis,* trans. W. R. Fisher. Oxford, England: Clarendon Press, 1903. Reprinted New York: Hafner Publishing Co., 1960.

Scott, D., and W. D. Billings. "The Effect of Environmental Factors on the Standing Crop and Productivity of an Alpine Tundra." *Ecological Monographs,* Vol. 34, pp. 243–270, 1964.

Sears, P. B. *Where There is Life.* New York: Dell Publishing Co., Inc., 1962.

Thomas, W. L., Jr., ed. *Man's Role in Changing the Face of the Earth.* Chicago: University of Chicago Press, 1956.

Weaver, J. E., and F. E. Clements. *Plant Ecology,* 2nd ed. New York: McGraw-Hill Book Company, 1938.

Wilsie, C. P. *Crop Adaptation and Distribution.* San Francisco: W. H. Freeman & Co., 1962.

Woodwell, G. M. "The Ecological Effects of Radiation." *Scientific American,* Vol. 208, pp. 40–49, 1963.

# GLOSSARY

**Alpine vegetation.** Low herbaceous or low shrubby vegetation above timberline in mountains.

**Arcto-Tertiary forest.** Forest of conifers and deciduous trees that covered northern parts of North America and Eurasia during middle of the Cenozoic Era. Known from fossils; age about 15–30 million years.

**Biomass.** Weight of living organisms in an ecosystem, expressed either as fresh weight or dry weight.

**Biotype.** Members of a local population with identical tolerance ranges; essentially a genotype.

**Boreal forest.** Northern spruce-fir-pine forest; the taiga.

**Broad-sclerophyll vegetation.** Vegetation dominated by angiosperm shrubs or trees with broad, leathery, evergreen leaves. Usually restricted to warm climates.

**Carnivore.** Meat-eating animal; member of third or fourth trophic levels in an ecosystem.

**Chaparral.** Dense vegetation of broad-sclerophyll shrubs characteristic of the mild "Mediterranean" climates of parts of California and the American Southwest.

**Chernozem.** Fertile black or dark brown soil under prairie or grassland with lime layer at some depth between 2 and 5 feet.

**Climax vegetation.** Relatively stable vegetation in equilibrium with its environment and with good reproduction of the dominant plants.

**Cold-air drainage.** Flowing of cold air down canyons and hillsides into valleys on calm, clear nights; results in temperature inversions.

**Community.** Plants and animals that live together and make up the biological part of an ecosystem.

**Competition.** Relative success of individuals in utilizing critical parts of the local environment. Also termed "interference."

**Decomposer.** Organism that utilizes dead plant or animal material for food and that releases the component elements to the environment, thus contributing to circulation of these elements in the ecosystem.

**Dominant.** Plant that, because of its foliage cover or extent of its root system, modifies and controls the local environment; usually many individuals constitute the dominant stratum—for example, pines in a pine forest.

**Ecocline.** Series of biotypes within a species that shows a genetic gradient correlated with a gradual environmental gradient.

**Ecological niche.**  Role of an organism in an ecosystem.

**Ecological race.**  Group of local populations within a species in which most individuals have similar environmental tolerances; wide-ranging species may consist of many ecological races.

**Ecological system.**  Energy-driven complex of one or more organisms and the environment.

**Ecologic range.**  Range of environmental conditions in which the members of a species actually live at present.

**Ecosystem.**  Energy-driven complex of a community of organisms and its controlling environment.

**Ecotone.**  Transition zone between two vegetational types or vegetational regions.

**Efficiency.**  Degree to which a plant or stand of vegetation converts radiant energy into organic compounds; efficiency may depend upon degree of utilization of necessary environmental components.

**Endemic species.**  Restricted to a relatively small geographic area or to an unusual or rare type of habitat.

**Energy budget.**  Disposition of radiant energy and heat in an environment.

**Environment.**  Sum of all external forces or influences that affect an organism.

**Epiphyte.**  Aerial plant that carries on photosynthesis but grows on another plant only for physical support; e.g., many orchids and mosses. Usually restricted to moist climates.

**Evaporation.**  Net loss of water molecules from liquid phase to vapor phase.

**Evapotranspiration.**  Combined evaporation and transpiration from a land surface and its plants.

**Flora.**  The kinds of plants present in a region.

**Food chain.**  The series of organisms through which food energy moves before it is completely expended.

**Garigue.**  Scrub vegetation of the Mediterranean region characterized by low shrubs, often of the mint and legume families, and aromatic herbs.

**Genotype.**  A certain genetic constitution characteristic of an individual or group of individuals that have been propagated vegetatively.

**Geographic range.**  Geographic limits of the ecologic range; geographic extent of actual occurrences of a species.

**Ground water.**  Free liquid water saturating all spaces at some depth below the surface of the ground. The top surface of the ground water is the "water table."

**Habitat.**  The specific kind of environment occupied by the individuals of a species.

**Heat budget.**  See *Energy budget.*

**Herbivore.**  Animal that eats plants.

**Holocoenotic principle.**  Principle that an environment acts as a whole unit because of lack of barriers to the interaction of its component factors; applicable also to an ecosystem.

**Hydrologic cycle.**   Precipitation, runoff, evapotranspiration of water cycle on the earth and in its atmosphere.

**Hydrophyte.**   Plant growing in water or dependent upon being partially immersed in liquid water at all times.

**Laterite.**   Reddish infertile tropical soil in which silica has been leached out, leaving a kaolinitic clay with a high content of iron and aluminum hydroxides.

**Lianas.**   Vines with woody stems; common in forests of warm climates.

**Life form.**   The vegetative size, structure, and appearance of a plant, such as a tree, a shrub, a grasslike plant.

**Light.**   Electromagnetic radiation of relatively short wavelengths, visible to the eye; about 400–760 millimicrons.

**Limiting factor.**   Environmental factor limiting the growth or reproduction of an individual or a community.

**Live oak woodland.**   Relatively open woods or forest dominated by evergreen oaks.

**Local population.**   Group of individuals of the same species growing near enough to each other to interbreed and exchange genes.

**Macchia.**   Same as maquis.

**Madro-Tertiary vegetation.**   Subtropical woodland vegetation occupying much of southwestern North America in the middle of the Cenozoic Era; known from fossils. Similar to present vegetation in the Sierra Madre of Mexico.

**Maquis.**   Broad-sclerophyll scrubby vegetation of the Mediterranean region similar to the chaparral of California.

**Mesophyte.**   Plant requiring intermediate moisture conditions; not very resistant to drought.

**Net radiation.**   Difference between incoming radiation (solar and sky) and outgoing thermal radiation at the earth's surface. Net radiation is that energy available for evaporation and convection, and for heating the soil.

**Paleoecology.**   Study of ecosystems of the past.

**Parent material.**   Mineral or organic material that weathers into a soil under the influence of climate and vegetation.

**Permafrost.**   Permanently frozen ground.

**Phenotype.**   The physical characteristics of an organism, the product of interaction between genotype and environment.

**Photosynthesis, gross.**   The total amount of food synthesized by a green plant from carbon dioxide and water in a given amount of time.

**Photosynthesis, net.**   The net amount of food synthesized by a green plant in a given amount of time after subtracting the amount used in respiration during that same time.

**Phreatophyte.**   Plant dependent upon ground water as opposed to soil moisture (e.g., willows, cottonwoods, mesquite, greasewood).

**Podzol.**   Acid soil in which surface soil is strongly leached of bases and clays.

**Population.**   Group of related individuals capable of interbreeding. A local population occurs in a relatively small geographic area and, because of usual ease of interbreeding, is the basic evolutionary unit.

**Productivity.**   Rate of dry-matter production by photosynthesis in an ecosystem.

**Propagule.**   Any part of a plant capable of growing into a new plant: a seed, spore, rhizome, or even a twig, leaf, or root in some species.

**Puszta.**   The Hungarian grassland, similar to the North American prairie.

**Rain shadow.**   Dry area in lee of mountains caused by descent and warming of air.

**Savanna.**   Tall grassland (usually tropical), often with scattered small trees or patches of woodland.

**Soil.**   Complex system of mineral, organic, water, and gaseous components produced from parent material by action of climate and vegetation.

**Soil moisture.**   Water held in the soil by capillary and hygroscopic forces. Most plants can utilize only the capillary soil moisture.

**Soil profile.**   The structure and composition of a soil as seen in the side of a pit, trench, or road-cut; made up of layers or horizons produced by leaching and deposition.

**Solar radiation.**   Any radiation from the sun—for example, high energy, ultraviolet, visible, or long wavelength radiation.

**Steady-state conditions.**   State in which the inflow of energy and materials in an ecosystem is just sufficient to maintain biomass at a relatively constant level.

**Succession.**   Change in composition of vegetation at a given location through time.

**Symbionts.**   Organisms living together and deriving mutual advantages by the association.

**Temperature.**   Measure of the tendency of a substance to give up heat.

**Temperature inversion.**   Warm air overlying colder air.

**Thermal radiation.**   Long wavelength or infrared radiation.

**Timberline.**   Limit of tree growth on a mountain or in the subarctic.

**Tolerance range.**   Range of environmental conditions in which an organism can survive; mainly set genetically but modified by previous environmental history of the individual.

**Trigger factor.**   A changed factor (or a new factor) that sets off a chain of events in an environment or in an ecosystem.

**Trophic level.**   Energy level in the food chain of an ecosystem.

**Tundra.**   Arctic or alpine vegetation beyond timberline.

**Vegetation.**   The actual plant covering of an area.

**Water-holding capacity.**   Amount of water a soil can hold against the pull of gravity; the "field capacity."

**Xerophyte.**   Plant capable of surviving extended drought.

# INDEX